Journey
to a
Greek
Island

Elias Kulukundis

CASSELL · LONDON

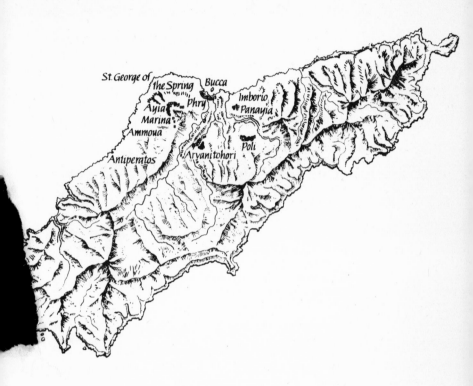

St. George of
the Spring
Bucca
Phry
Imborio
Panayia
Ayia
Marina
Ammoua
Antiperatos
Aryanitohori
Poli

Journey
to a Greek Island

CASSELL & COMPANY LTD
35 Red Lion Square, London WC1
Melbourne, Sydney, Toronto
Johannesburg, Auckland

Copyright © 1967 by Elias Kulukundis
First published in Great Britain 1968

S.B.N. 304 93203 5

Printed in Great Britain by Cox & Wyman Ltd,
London, Fakenham and Reading

F.568

To my father and mother

and to Uncle George

Preface

Ever since I began this book, people have asked me, "Is it a novel? A travel book? An autobiography?" I suppose the last comes closest: it is an autobiography of everything that did not happen to me.

People who are familiar with Kasos and its stories will protest that everything did not happen the way I say. They are right. I make no claim to "objective truth." On the contrary, I believe for everyone there is a different Kasos. This one is mine. If it does not square with someone else's, I make no apology.

In the chapters on the history of the island, I made use of material in the following books: *History of the Greek Revolution* by Thomas Gordon, *History of Greece* by George Finlay, *History of Kasos* by T. Evangelidou and M. Michailidou-Nouarou, *The Island of Roses and her Eleven Sisters* by Michael Volonakis, *Italy's Aegean Possessions* by Booth and Booth, the files of *The Dodecanesian,* published by the Dodecanesian League of America and the Dodecanesian National Council.

For material on the origin of the naming customs as well as their connection to inheritance, I am indebted to *Legal Customs of the Dodecanese* by M. Michailidou-Nouarou. The theory of the *vrykolakas* and its connection with vendetta, I owe to *Modern Greek Folklore and Ancient Greek Religion* by John Cuthbert Lawson. For material on the various other customs of the island, I am indebted to *Kasiotika,* a collection of Kasiot lore by the Reverend Zacharias Halkiades, and I am grateful to the author for personally answering my questions.

No one could write on any subject of the Dodecanese without drawing on the work of Dr. Nicholas Mavris. (An early partisan of *Enosis,* he was later elected Governor of Rhodes and representative from the Dodecanese in the Greek Parliament.) I am indebted to his *Historical Archive of Kasos, Dodecanesian Bibliography, Dodecanesian Lyre* (a collection of Dodecanesian songs and rhymes), as well as other pamphlets and articles. Moreover, I am especially grateful for the many hours he spent with me, for his kindness in throwing open his personal library and otherwise directing me to sources I required, and for his friendly encouragement.

I cannot name all the Kasiots—relatives and friends—who sat down with me to answer my questions and share their memories, but I am grateful to all of them. I am also grateful to friends and colleagues who read my manuscript and gave me advice and comments.

Contents

Journey
to a
Greek
Island

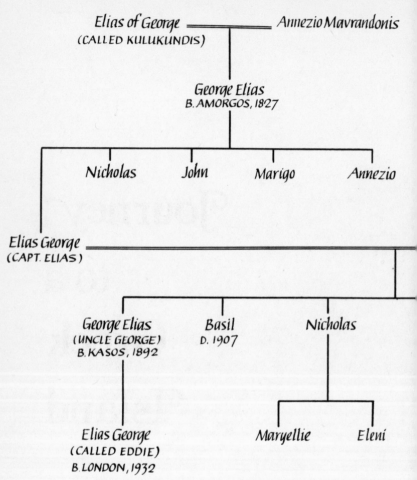

KULUKUNDIS

Elias of George ————————— Annezio Mavrandonis
(CALLED KULUKUNDIS)

George Elias
B. AMORGOS, 1827

Nicholas   John   Marigo   Annezio

Elias George ————————————————————
(CAPT. ELIAS)

George Elias   Basil   Nicholas
(UNCLE GEORGE)   D. 1907
B. KASOS, 1892

Elias George   Maryellie   Eleni
(CALLED EDDIE)
B. LONDON, 1932

★ As a fourth son, Manuel should have been named for his mother's oldest brother, but the names of Eleni's first three brothers would have caused duplications. He was named finally for his mother's fourth brother.

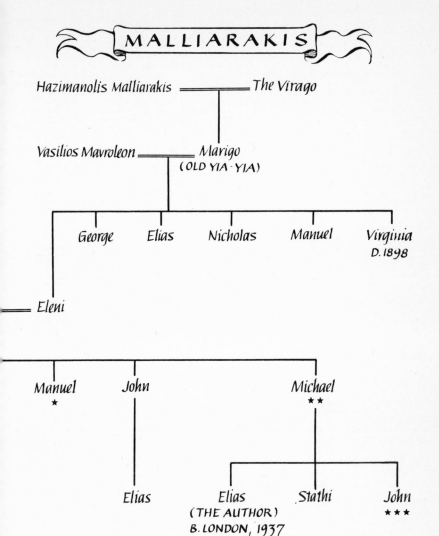

MALLIARAKIS

Hazimanolis Malliarakis ═══════ The Virago

Vasilios Mavroleon ═══════ Marigo
(OLD YIA·YIA)

George   Elias   Nicholas   Manuel   Virginia
D. 1898

═══ Eleni

Manuel   John   Michael
★   ★★

Elias   Elias   Stathi   John
(THE AUTHOR)   ★★★
B. LONDON, 1937

★★   By this time the names of Eleni's family had all been used, and she
      had free choice, a rare case in Kasiot history.

★★★   This third son was named after his father's closest brother.

This Family Tree includes only the names of people relevant to the naming custom or mentioned in the text.

Arrival

I did not see Kasos until I was twenty-seven, when I made this journey. I have never lived there, and neither have my parents. They were born on Syros, another island two hundred miles up the Aegean. I was born in London, came to America when I was three, and have lived here ever since.

Only my grandparents were native Kasiots, all four of them. My grandfathers were sea captains, and at the turn of the century they emigrated to Syros, then the largest port in Greece. After the First World War, they emigrated to a still larger port: London. My father and his brothers took over the shipping business their father had begun. And eventually, in 1939, my parents extended the emigration farther to America. They settled in Rye, a suburb of New York, where I spent all but the first three years of childhood.

This journey will be back along the course of that emigration. The destination is Kasos, the final island. On the way back we come first to Syros, capital and metropolis of the Cyclades. Syros was where my parents met for the first time, when my father was six years old, my mother an infant. It was at my mother's christening. My mother was in her godfather's arms; my father was standing beside his own mother, the youngest in a row of five brothers ranging from ages six to twenty. They met in a house filled with relatives and neighbors on a mountainside of scrubbed white houses, rising like an amphitheater before the ever various spectacle of the Aegean Sea. At the windows of that house, looking southward down the Archipelago, we are two hundred miles from Kasos and one generation still to go.

Syros, like London, was a way-station in the journey. My grandparents lived there as immigrants, as almost everyone in Syros was at one time. Except for a thousand natives, Syros was settled by people of other islands—Chios, Psara, Crete, and Kasos—made homeless during the Greek Revolution against the Turks. Much later, at the end of the nineteenth century, my grandparents sailed to this first America. At the time, there was already a Kasiot quarter waiting for them, just as they were Chiot and Psariot quarters. As Kasiot children, my parents felt different from the other children of Syros, just as they were later to feel as adults in London, and their own children were to feel in Rye, New York.

But if my parents are not true natives of Syros, still it was their beginning. My mother's father built a villa in the hills, and my parents have helped preserve it ever since his death and returned to it for the last twelve summers. They have preserved it as a memorial to their parents and their childhood, a reminder of what they were before they embarked on outward voyages to begin their life together in an alien land, then raise their children in yet another one.

It is a familiar story in a Greek life. Exile is a Greek experience, and there is even a Greek word for it which does not exist in other languages. It is *xenitia,* which is not exactly exile because it can be self-imposed, and not estrangement because there is no spiritual estrangement. *Xenitia* is simply the loss of the native land. It is an old experience in the Greek mind, as old as the pre-Christian Greeks who spread from the native peninsula in an ever widening diaspora to other shores of the Mediterranean, the Red Sea, and the Black. Despite this sense of exile which haunts him to the grave, the Greek is ever journeying, especially the islander, who is hemmed in only by the horizon. This Greek is ever arriving or departing, on the way out, or on the way back. No sooner did my parents take the outward journey than the horizon opened toward their way home. No sooner did they cross a continent to Europe and an ocean to New York but they repeated the journey in the reverse direction, performing it in a continual celebration of the same event, a perennial round trip of reconciliation and farewell.

But my journey back was different. I had no memory of Syros, no image of a native island, of a villa with a red gabled roof and groves of olive, orange, and lemon trees descending from it on orderly terraces of land. When I awoke to memory, Syros was beyond me. The first place I remember is a room in a country club in Rye, New York, where my parents had come to live. That country club is a huge stone edifice erupted out of the suburban landscape. It has statues and porticoes, vaults and gargoyles; and to this day I wonder how my parents ever found it. To Greek immigrants it must have been the epitome of strangeness.

"Here is America," my father must have thought, as he settled down with his family in a cavernous fortress from "A Diamond as Big as the Ritz." Here, in this gigantic relic of a lost America, my Greek childhood began. Downstairs, in a vaulted dining room, my parents sat with friends and relatives around an oval table, most of them not only Greeks but Kasiots, concentrating on their American hotel food in the inviolate silence of the Greek at table. And upstairs, by windows that overlooked an outdoor dance floor and ultimately a golf course, I lay in bed, puzzling out the arabesques on my carpeted, hotel floor.

After some months, my parents bought a house nearby, and before long I never thought to ask how we had arrived there. I did not think of journeys then, because for a child there are no arrivals and departures, no past and future, only *now*. Only years later was I to see Syros. In the meantime, I had to understand as best I could that I lived in a Greek house in Rye, New York. It was a house in Rye, where the Greek language was spoken, and Greek food was on the table, and Greek people gathered in the evening, after an hour's drive from New York City, sitting together in their *xenitia* before a window that overlooked the golf course and the hills of Westchester.

As for Greece, in the meantime, I knew nothing of it. As a nation it was slumbering in my mind, just as it had slumbered for centuries in the Ottoman Empire before awakening in 1821 to discover itself. Through those years of darkness, the same agents were at work on me as had worked on the medieval subjects of the Sultan: parents, priests, and teachers. They taught me its language, religion, and history; but none of them succeeded in convincing me that it really existed anywhere. The only Greece I could believe in was the Greece I knew. Greece was downstairs in our house in Rye, as I sat by the bannister on the second floor, watching the people in our living room, listening to their babel of words and laughter. Greece was downstairs on a Sunday night, while upstairs, in America, I answered questions in my workbook before going to bed. Greece was Monday and Thursday afternoons when a Greek teacher arrived on the train from New York City to teach me the pluperfect and future perfect of Greek verbs when elsewhere, in America, other children were playing baseball. Greece was the church I went to, where there were icons with mournful faces. Greece was the nights when there were guests, familiar yet unrecognizable, speaking in obscure liquid syllables. Greece was when my mother served tiny meatballs, vine-leaves with meat and rice inside, and a soup of egg and lemon that tasted different a moment after you swallowed it. Greece was afterward, when I lay in bed and heard the train of voices rumbling on beneath me: a low subterranean echo of another life.

It was not really Greece, only its echo sounding through the corridors of war and emigration. I did not see the real Greece until I was seventeen, when I emerged from my tunnel of ignorance into the shining reality at its end, like that underground river which began in Hades and flowed out of the abode of darkness to the sea. That was in 1954, when after fifteen years of *xenitia*, my parents first returned to the island of their birth.

That summer, sailing southeast from Athens' port city, Piraeus, I first saw the island of Syros. It lay horizontally before the ship, the prow intersecting it as though for landfall. But however long we sailed toward it, we seemed to reach no closer. For hours it lay before us: receding, chimerical. Finally, as we began to overtake it, we could make out only a spine of mountains, betraying no sign of life: a whitened skeleton, petrified with age. As we rounded the northeastern tip, the island began to recede again, hiding behind a rocky cliff. After so many hours of distance, we were perilously close, within a hundred yards of bottomless blue water. And still there was no sign of life. Still the island could be an abandoned relic, picked clean by centuries of Aegean pirates.

Now, as the land loomed up suddenly beside us, there was a crowd at the rail. A hush had fallen on the ship and we could hear each throb of the slackening engines as silently the land slipped by. Everyone was waiting, because a voyage has a natural drama of its own and its climax is the landfall. We followed the scaly promontory, verging toward it so that it seemed eventually we must collide against its rocks. And behind it somewhere was the island, out of sight, elusive to the last. Still there was no sign of life. Still Syros was a heap of ash, reddened in the setting sun: a volcanic cinder in a timeless sea.

Then, at last, it happened. I was standing with my father at the rail, and afterward he told me he had been expecting it. He remembered it from the countless landfalls of his childhood. But for me it was happening for the first time, and the first blast took me by surprise. It was the ship's whistle, sounding over that island of the dead like the last trumpet. The first few moments, I saw and heard nothing, waiting for it to be over. But it wasn't over. Long moments it sustained itself, growing louder: a chord struck on a maddened organ. Then at last it was gone. Sight and sound returned to us assaulted passengers. And when I looked at the island, a lonely chapel had appeared on a cliff above the ship, as though summoned to existence by the whistle itself. In the limpid air above us, it seemed a benign augury, returning our salute with the chapel bell, tinkling in the silence. The next moment, the engines paused suddenly and with our momentum lost, the land wind swept across the ship. It brought the smell of thyme growing on those barren hillsides, the smell of land. Syros was alive. It had been called forth from the world of ghosts and fantasies: it existed. A moment later, the land itself abandoned its long resistance to our ship: the promontory fell away and we turned the corner, into an audience of chalk-white houses gathered around the harbor.

The whistle was still sounding in my ears. For my father it was a benign greeting, a welcome home. But for me it was the shrill apprehension of arrival on an unknown shore. The Greek Revolution began in 1821; mine began in 1954, and that ship's whistle was the signal for the conflict to begin, for images to clash together, between a Greece that had been and a Greece that was.

We were driven up to the villa in the hills. At every turning, the driver blew his horn, hardly slackening his speed, so that all the way up the winding road, another insistent trumpet continued the alarm. Beyond the final turning, we could see a rim of mountains unfold against the sky, and my mother pointed to lights in the distance beyond a cavernous valley.

It was the villa, still there after fifteen years. My grandfather was gone, dead since 1942. Now the villa's mistresses were three Kasiot women, my mother's great aunts, sisters of my mother's grandmother. It was as though the compounded catastrophes of war and exile had simply reversed the normal pattern of inheritance so that the house was acquired not by the younger generation but by the older.

"They can see us," my mother said, for she knew, ever since the ship's whistle had sounded and the driver had descended to the town, the three old women would be standing at the gate.

And they were. There were three black shadows against the ornate latticed door, with a retinue of servants around them. They wore black robes blowing in the wind, and loose black cowls shrouding their faces.

Those three women were my first view of Kasos, though it would be another ten years before I actually arrived there. I saw my first glimpse of Kasos that night in Syros, as a boy of seventeen, arriving on this implausible summer excursion to confront three hooded figures on a hilltop of the past.

In the weeks to come, I realized that my aunts were strangers in Syros. Their black robes and cowls set them apart even from the older population; they spoke Greek in an unfamiliar accent, and used words the Syriots did not understand. Then I realized that even these three old women were living out a *xenitia*. They too were in exile, and the surrounding hills of Syros were as irrelevant to them and to their place of origin as the hills of Westchester to my parents. In my journey to the past, I had reached only a way-station, the same one where my grandparents had stopped, arriving in Syros from the opposite direction. My arrival in Syros was a false arrival. Syros was a vantage point from which another journey extended outward, toward an island which could only be imagined beyond the remaining expanse of time and sea.

But that summer I got no farther. I returned as other seventeen year olds to a final year in an American school, headed for an American college. Afterward, there followed more years of *xenitia*, and the black Kasiot granddames receded again into the world of dream. I was twenty-seven, when I set out again, resolved to make the journey to its end.

In the meantime, I managed to learn a little more of Greece. Once I discovered it was actually a country, I began to read about it the same way I might read of France and England. I started with the present and read backward, a natural method since the first Greece I knew was downstairs in my house. In the same way, I learned more of the Greek language, giving form to countless sounds and syllables existing amorphously in my mind.

"Do you speak Romaic?" those familiar strangers in my father's house used to ask me.

The first time, I didn't know what to answer. If they meant did I speak Greek, I would have made a brave attempt to get the endings right and said: "Yes, I speak Greek." But what was Romaic? I had never heard of it. So I shook my head, and they laughed and said, "Shame on you, not to speak Romaic."

Finally, they asked me so many times that I began to suspect *Romaic* must have something to do with *Greek*. When they asked me again, I smiled and said, "Yes, I speak Romaic." And they too smiled and said, "*Bravo*, you're a good boy who speaks Romaic."

After that I troubled my head no more over the meaning of *Romaic*. It was just another word for Greek which adults had used perversely to confuse me. Then, recently, I learned that

Romaic is the language spoken by modern Greeks, as distinguished from the *Hellenic* of the ancients. After the fall of Constantinople, the citizens of the fallen Byzantine Empire were known to their Turkish masters as *Romaioi* (Romans), their language as *Romaic*.

"*Ti haparia?*" I heard my parents say, greeting friends, "What *haparia?*" or as I translated by intuition, "What news?" As good a mimic as any child, I took up the greeting: "Hello," I would say to my parents' friends, "*Ti haparia?*"

Eventually, I learned the word *hapari* does mean news, but it is a Turkish word which in its original meaning was applied strictly to news of death. So, taking the etymology far enough, what I was really saying in those cheerful greetings of my childhood was: "What news of death can I expect from you? Who do you know in Charon's kingdom now?"

In the same way, I began to unravel stories I had been hearing all my life, stories of events which had taken place on Kasos in my grandparents' time and earlier. Of my father's family, everyone except him and another brother were born on Kasos, and with these relatives constantly visiting my house in Rye, there was ample opportunity for me to hear of it. I learned much of it from my parents, for in a Greek family stories have a way of being handed on, and even though my parents had never lived in Kasos, they could tell me what they knew of it from their own parents and grandparents. In this way, over the years. I assembled what I know of Kasos, adding something here and there, until some pattern of the island must emerge, like the mosaics made of smooth black and white pebbles on the floors of island courtyards.

In addition, I made a journey to the island myself, an actual journey. To make it, I needed a guide and mentor, for on any journey of discovery, the traveler needs someone to accompany him who has been before and knows the way. For me, this guide and mentor was the eldest of my father's brothers, my Uncle George. He had come to New York when we did. And before that, he had arrived in London at the same time as my parents and grandparents. But in addition, he had made the emigration to Syros. Unlike my parents, he was born in Kasos, in 1892, and when his father and mother journeyed northward in 1899, Uncle George was watching Kasos disappear behind him.

It is hard to imagine him as he was then, so I must start with what I first remember of him, in Rye, New York. As we played in our yard on a summer afternoon, my brothers and I would hear the sound of digging. Then, above the hedge that enclosed the vegetable garden, Uncle George would rear up from his labors. He wore overalls like the Farmer in the Dell; his shoulders were stooped and his cherub face was glowing with the heat and the merry embarrassment of being discovered at some mischief.

"Ah, there you are, Uncle George!" we said.

And Uncle George replied, "Yes, there you are Uncle George!"

Without condescension or pretense, Uncle George was so much a child himself that we accepted him into the exclusive and magic fraternity of our childhood. He was not a grown-up, not really an uncle, either. In fact, to tease us, he used to call us all Uncle.

"Uncle Stathi," he called my brother, which made my brother very angry.

"I'm not *Uncle* Stathi," my brother would protest. "I'm just plain Stathi."

And Uncle George, too, was just plain Uncle George. On a Sunday morning, we would see him tramping across our lawn in his baggy business suit with the belt buckled up high around his waist, his shoulders rounded over in a perfect curve.

"You'll stay for lunch, Uncle George," we said, taking him by the hand.

"No, I cannot," Uncle George would say, holding back, beaming with mischief.

"Why not, Uncle George?"

"Because you have no food."

"But we do! But we do, Uncle George."

"You do?" said Uncle George. "Well then, I'll stay."

He usually brought some contraption with him, some quixotic project we would pursue with him for an entire Sunday afternoon. Once it was a parachute he had bought from Army-Navy surplus.

"You're not going to make the children jump off the roof are you?" my mother said.

"Of course not!" said Uncle George.

"Of course not!" we said, echoing his indignation, though with Uncle George, we weren't entirely sure.

But Uncle George was true to his word. Instead, out of the attic window, fastened to the straps of the parachute, he threw out one of my father's best leather suitcases.

On another occasion, he brought a kit for making plaster statues: a quantity of rubber to be melted down and made into a mold, and a plaster composition to be made into the statue. Uncle George borrowed a saucepan from my mother, then led us to a workshop in the cellar. He stood over the pan of bubbling rubber like a sorcerer.

"I know," he said, "We'll make a copy of Stathi's cat."

Stathi brought a porcelain cat which Uncle George remembered seeing in his room. And as we two sorcerer's apprentices looked over his shoulder, Uncle George poured molten rubber over it.

The porcelain cat was ruined. If it exists anywhere today, it has a brown rubber stripe running down its back. But by the end of the afternoon, there were dozens of other cats to take its place, dozens of white plaster likenesses, all imperfect copies of the original. With each new birth, Stathi or I would run upstairs to show it to my parents. One cat had no ears, another no tail. There were blind cats, lame cats, headless cats. In a few hours, they had come out of our cellar like a plague.

Stathi hurried back to the workshop where the kindly wizard was continuing his work.

"No more cats," said Stathi.

"What?" said Uncle George.

"My mother says no more cats. She says we already have too many cats."

And so we did. There were cats on every table, by every chair. They lurked behind sofas, stood brazenly on doorsteps. As creator of that bizarre litter, Uncle George felt he must make amends.

"We'll take them to church," he said.

"What for?" we said.

"So the ladies can sell them at the spring bazaar."

But it was no use. In three weeks, all the cats were back, each one swaddled in newspaper. The ladies of the parish thanked us but regretted to inform us that not one cat had been sold.

With such a record of quixotic adventure, Uncle George was bound to come on my journey. This time, he had no responsibility for the project, since I was the one to initiate it. But he took a certain risk in helping me. He told me so much about Kasos in the days of his parents and grandparents that like the cats he let out of our cellar, I am afraid some things will return to be laid at his door.

But in the summer of 1964, he set out with me for Kasos. By that time, he was living in Greece again, working in a shipping office in Piraeus. After twenty years in London and another twenty in New York, he had turned his outward journey back upon itself. Now, accompanying an insistent and inquiring nephew, he would retrace that journey to its first departure, to visit Kasos for the first time since 1910 when he had gone back as a young man of eighteen in a white naval uniform and a black moustache.

To get to Kasos we had to take a ship from Crete. There were three of us, Uncle George and I, and my cousin, another Elias, son of my father's brother John, who was born and raised in London. Like most Greek first cousins who are eldest sons, he and I have the same first name because we are both named for our father's father, Captain Elias, who lived in Kasos with his wife Eleni.

When we arrived in Crete, we realized that we had no presents to bring our Kasiot hosts, some small token to commemorate our visit. Uncle George had a vast assortment of objects in his suitcase, for he is an incorrigible saver: plastic bags which had once enclosed new shirts, a bottle of cleaning fluid wrapped in a piece of heavy rubber tubing, an endless supply of cotton, pencils, toothpicks, and bits of rubberbands. But nothing suitable for presents.

As the journey neared its end, we were dreading what the Kasiots would have to say about us, the satirical couplets called *mandinadhas* they would compose about our stinginess, to be sung to the whining of a lyre in the cafe. Then, as we were driving to Ayios Nikolaos, the port where we were to meet the ship, my uncle saw a clump of bananas hanging in front of a fruit vendor's shop.

We stopped the car, and Uncle George got out to inspect the bananas.

"Shall we buy them?" he said, but I knew it was a false question. Once he had such an idea, it would chase itself around in his head and nothing you might say to him would make any difference. We bought the bananas. I was chosen to take charge of them, since I had just cleverly re-arranged my hand-luggage so that I had one free hand. Now, in that free hand, I carried a giant clump of bananas to the car, a huge stalk with dozens of unripened bananas growing out of it.

"Well, at least we'll have some presents now," I said to my uncle as the car started up again. "When we come ashore in Kasos, I can carry the banana-tree and you can break off the bananas and pass them out among the people."

"You think so?" replied my uncle. "That would be worse than no presents, since obviously they would misunderstand and compose even nastier couplets at our expense."

Now Uncle George is never one to explain what he means. If you do not understand, he will just wait for you to ask him and then supply an explanation. But by that time, I had asked him so many questions, I was beginning to feel like Glaucon in the dialogues, posing ingenuous questions as cues for the Socratic homilies.

Now, on the subject of bananas, it was time for such a cue.

"Why, Uncle?" I said.

"Why?" said my uncle. "I'll tell you why."

And so, Socratically, my uncle explained why Kasiots might misunderstand our giving them bananas. In the islands as well as the rural areas of mainland Greece, it is indecorous to mention anything of phallic shape. A peasant, speaking of a cucumber or a squash, would feel he owed his listener an apology.

"Begging your pardon," he would say, "the cucumbers in our village grow to be that long." Or, "Our squashes—by your indulgence—are not out yet."

Now things took a turn for the worse, as I saw the true significance of that phenomenon rearing up beside me on the seat. If you could not mention a single banana in polite company, what could you say about an entire banana-tree? What would I say when I disembarked at Kasos, risen from the sea, with a hundred bananas held on high?

When we arrived in Ayios Nikolaos, Uncle George and I tried to do something about our bananas. We got a paper carton from the café keeper and borrowed a jacknife from an American tourist. Then, ruthlessly, Uncle George cut off all the bananas and packed them away in the carton. Now I would not need to apologize as I stepped ashore at Kasos.

The tourist was amazed at us. Why were we cutting off the bananas? It's a long story, I thought. Where did those bananas come from? He had never seen such tiny ones. Doesn't matter, I thought, the size has nothing to do with it.

The ship set out at dawn. Beyond the eastern tip of Crete, we crossed the straits the sailing ships had passed through with cargoes bound for Egypt. That was the unprotected stretch of sea where during the Revolution every captain unfriendly to the cause of Greece cast an uneasy eye around him, dreading to see a speck on the horizon which would emerge into a Kasiot bow and sail.

But now, in 1964, the sea was empty. Crete was fading behind us, and ahead there was horizon all around, vacant and unbroken. I was on the bridge with Uncle George, waiting for Kasos to materialize. In a low murmur every so often obliterated by the wind, he explained the principles of navigation. He must have been remembering other days at sea, imagining that after an outward voyage of fifty years, he was navigating this homeward landfall himself.

But my mind was not on navigation. It was on the horizon ahead of us. I knew we must be just halfway, and since the coast of Crete had just disappeared behind us, Kasos should appear at any moment.

For an instant I thought I saw a rim of mountains outlined against the sky, a penciled curve against the obscure confluence of sky and sea. But when I blinked, the line was gone. I saw nothing but the light mist that hung on the horizon like the vapors of the morning. Even now, if it were there at all, Kasos was a phantom.

Then, suddenly, it was there. It had become, out of that obscurity of sky and sea exactly in the form of that first elusive vision. It had been there all along. I had been seeing it for several minutes, if only I had believed my eyes.

Gradually, it grew more distinct, emerging from the heat-blur on the horizon, the folds of sky and sea separating around it. As we came closer, we saw waves breaking on the rocky coast, marking the boundaries of the land with an unbroken ring of white, confirming the ancient name the Phoenicians had given it: *Kas,* the isle of sea-foam. Gradually we saw coves and turnings on the impenetrable coast, the land cascading sharply into bottomless blue water. The island itself appeared completely bald, like a mountain peak, which in fact it is. Halfway up the northern coast, we saw the first signs of life: the crisscrossing of the dry-stone walls, protecting each narrow lace of land from ravages of the goats; then mills, abandoned and shorn of blades, lined up the barren slopes in a decapitated phalanx; at last we saw houses, tiny white squares on top of a hill, like gravestones.

We approached the landfall obliquely, making for a set of islands off the northern coast. As we neared them, they separated one behind the other like unjoining bones. Past Armathia, the largest island, we turned to starboard, aiming for a small harbor still invisible which I knew to be the only niche in the iron-bound Kasiot coast. Along the shore, there was a group of houses which must be the town of Phry. Beyond, we could see the other towns, Panayia, Poli, Arvanitohori, and Ayia Marina, all laid out on that scant plateau beneath the mountains, like eggs in the corners of an apron.

Remembering the landfall at Syros, I waited for the town of Phry to unfold around the harbor. As we came closer, I thought the houses were just a suggestion of the town, the rear of it turned seaward. They were all low and square, some a faded white, others grayish brown. Some were but the ghosts of houses: empty windows in a four-walled frame, enclosing nothing but the rubble of a caved-in roof. These were the husks of houses, the life shelled out of them, not by war or earthquake, but as surely and as inevitably as either one, by time and *xenitia*. At the center of the town were two breakwaters, with a narrow aperture between them leading into what had served for centuries as the only harbor on the island: the Bucca, named after the Italian word for mouth, sealed off from the sea by threatening, shrewish jaws. Beside the Bucca, on a rocky and embattled bastion, the Church of St. Spiridon presided with a belltower of faded blue, red and yellow, with a clock on its face marking the morning hour as incongruously as though it had been stopped for a hundred years.

We proceeded to the landfall, engines throbbing in the sudden silence, the sea audibly washing the iron coast a hundred yards or so away. We aimed a little east of the church and the houses, where the entrance to the harbor must be. There, as at Syros, we would round a promontory and make the turn. As on that first arrival, there would be an audience of houses suddenly revealed.

But the turning never came. There was no promontory for us to sail around, and there was no more to Phry. We had seen the town and passed it. The houses trailed off into a stoney wasteland, and a dirt road almost indistinguishable from the earth around it wound on farther toward an unattended harbor. The only audience for this landfall was a disorderly procession of people taking long silent strides toward the harbor, shielding off the sun with parasols and kicking up the dust. Five hundred yards later, without a turning, the ship slipped into the narrow receptacle which was our journey's end. At that moment, two jet planes of the Greek Air Force flew over the island before turning north to Rhodes: two scraping anachronisms, disfiguring an imagined sky.

We made our way through the chaos on the wharf. Under one arm, I carried a portable tape-recorder, under the other, balancing precariously, a boxed and corded cargo of forbidden fruit. To get to our house, we took one of the two automobiles on the island. Another clarion sounded through narrow streets. Chickens, goats, and donkeys fled before us. Children ran to stand beside their mothers, watching from doorways. As the town thinned out, the crumbling foundations sank once again into fields of rubble. The car rattled uphill toward Ayia Marina, then stopped before a row of dilapidated balconies which overlooked the sea. At the end of the row, by a light blue doorway in a wall of gypsum white, I recognized my grandmother's house.

It was the house where Uncle George and three of his brothers were born. No one in my family has lived there since 1899 when my grandparents, Captain Elias and Eleni, and four small boys embarked on that first emigration north to Syros. It was really two houses, with a veranda between them, presiding over a courtyard below. Around the whole compound was a high wall with a wooden gate leading to the street. The walls were all of blinding white gypsum, baked by the sun of a hundred summers. The doors and shutters were wood, painted light blue, so that the whole house was a sort of Greek flag—all light blue and white—a motif which must have rankled Kasos' erstwhile rulers, the Turks and the Italians.

At the gate to welcome us was an old woman who used to be Uncle George's nurse, brought originally from an orphanage to look after Eleni's first four children. She had left the family just after the emigration to Syros, to live out her own *xenitia* in Alexandria. Then, fifty years later, impoverished and stricken with arthritis, she returned to her adopted home in Kasos. For over a dozen years, she had lived alone in the house of the blue shutters which she called "My Eleni's house" though Eleni died in 1935 and she, the old woman, was its only mistress. For our arrival, she wore a bright checkered robe and a white kerchief around her head, and thick, goggle-like lenses. Her name—no more appropriate to the plump and saucy island girl than to the wrinkled woman on bandaged and arthritic feet—was Aphrodite.

"So you've decided to come," Aphrodite told my uncle. "And who are these you've brought?"

"Two Eliases," said Uncle George. "The sons of my brothers. Elias of John. And Elias of Michael."

Our lineage made no impression on her: our fathers were the last two of Eleni's sons, born in Syros after Aphrodite had left the family.

"So the two Eliases have come to Kasos too," she said, and turned inside the gate. Two silent Eliases entered after her.

She led us through the courtyard, beneath the two white houses presiding over it, up the stone stairway to the terrace between them set with smooth black and white Rhodian pebbles assembled by a traveling mosaic maker in the shape of a flower. From this terrace, which is like the bridge of a sailing ship, you could sweep your eyes across the Aegean Sea. Aphrodite dismissed it with a wave of her hand. "You should have come to see me in Alexandria," she said. "There I had a house of my own to live in, and another one which I made into a boarding house and Arab servants to wait on me and call me 'Kyra Aphrodite.' And then, my bad luck, I got sick so I couldn't run the house anymore, and I didn't have any money, and so I asked your uncle what I should do and he said, 'Go back to Kasos. Go back to the old house.'"

"I said that?" said Uncle George. "On the contrary, I knew you would be unhappy here but you insisted on coming back."

"Insisted on coming back? Why should I insist on coming back to this pile of rubble?"

It was an old dispute between them. Actually, Uncle George was right: he had advised her not to come but she insisted, and now, altering her memory of the facts, she blamed him for all her ills. They quarreled about it constantly throughout our stay. In fact, they quarreled about everything. The relations one forms in childhood can endure a lifetime, and so for Uncle George, Aphrodite was not an old woman to be indulged and pitied, but the sharp-tongued island girl who had led him to the washbasin when he was a boy.

We went into the second house, where no one—not even Aphrodite—had lived since 1899. We followed its custodian, as though entering a newly opened tomb. This house had become Eleni's when she married, built originally for Eleni's mother, Old Yia-Yia (Old Grandmother), as Uncle George's son, Eddie, called her in his childhood to distinguish her from Eleni who would be simply Yia-Yia (Grandmother). It was built in the European style, unlike the other house which at one time had the raised platform and latticed railing of Turkish bedrooms. It had a living room called a *salla*, chairs and sofas instead of Turkish cushions, and designs on the walls and ceiling, painted by a traveling artist from Smyrna. On one wall, framed and pressed under glass, there was a piece of needlework, a skill which every Kasiot maiden must master. Beneath it was Old Yia-Yia's embroidered signature and a date which was almost an exact century from the time of our arrival: Marigo Malliarakis, 1863.

Now, in the privacy of our house, with the doors closed and windows shuttered, we unpacked the bananas and spread them out on the windowsill. And in the days to come, some of them came to a mysterious end. The next evening Aphrodite came in on her bandaged feet to explain that four bananas had slipped off the windowsill. She said they fell to the floor, and rotted instantly, and she had to dispose of them. My uncle acknowledged the fact without comment, ("Fine, Aphrodite, fine," he said) but I remember, at the time, I wondered why she should make such a laborious and implausible explanation. The next afternoon, instead of going into my bedroom where I usually slept, I happened to lie down on a sofa behind the doorway to the living room. My book had just slipped from my fingers and I was sinking into the moist and sultry somnolence of the Greek afternoon, when suddenly I heard a padded step on the threshold. It was Aphrodite, coming out of her room at an hour when she thought everyone must be asleep, stepping lightly into the living room and the alcove where the bananas lay on the windowsill. She thought I was asleep, and I lay motionless, watching her. She ate six bananas, peeling them one by one, devouring them almost whole. Then, licking her lips, she crept out again, like a sated wolf.

I was just thinking of what I would tell my uncle, when there was another sound on the threshold and I closed my eyes again and pretended to be asleep. It was another visitor braving that hour of the afternoon when every Kasiot house was still. This one was in his undershirt. His belt was buckled high above his waist, and his back was rounded in a perfect curve, as he filled his already puffy and cherubic cheeks with that unmentionable yet celebrated fruit.

On our first afternoon in Kasos, we searched Eleni's house. We found photographs in an old safe manufactured in Marseilles, and letters stuffed into silverware and crockery packed in old wedding chests. But the greatest treasure we discovered was a photograph known in my family as the *Hectodactylon,* literally, The Sixth Dactyl. It was a photograph of my uncle, taken according to the Kasiot custom of photographing a newborn baby so that the gender is apparent. My uncle had bare feet; his skirt was raised slightly; his foot was drawn up between his legs: so that a careful scrutiny revealed a sixth toe.

Then we went out onto the terrace above the courtyard. The sun was reddening the sky towards Crete. Across from us, as though we were sailing toward them, the mountains of Karpathos rose from the sea, into a nimbus of mist.

"Look down there," said Aphrodite, pointing to the courtyard. The stones were cracked now, a huge stump protruded among them, marking the place where, in my uncle's childhood, a large pine tree had stood high over the house.

"Eleni was crowned in marriage here. In this courtyard, Elias Kulukundis paid his call to the family of his future bride, concluding his engagement. A week later, they were crowned together beneath this sky, and this courtyard was all rice and sugared almonds. Then, the first child was born, and the townspeople waited for the midwife to come out and stand on the terrace, holding the child against the sky. And according to the custom, she gave out a false announcement to deceive any evil spirits. 'It's a girl!' she said, though with the child held naked above them, everyone could see it wasn't so, that Eleni's firstborn was a man-child and his name was George!"

"Yes," I thought, "with a sixth toe to prove it."

"Then, later," Aphrodite continued, "the christening was held within these same four walls. The Priest came up from St. Spiridon to perform the service. And someone on the balcony— I forget who it was—picked up a handful of mezitia° and flung them into the sky above the courtyard, so that on George's christening, the sky was raining money. And let me tell you, that was the last time it has been raining money anywhere near your uncle. He's so stingy, he can't find a pound or two to keep the walls and shutters painted on his mother's house."

"Stingy?" came Uncle George's voice from inside the living room. "I'm always sending you money, more than you know what to do with."

A wind had come up, and across from us, the peaks of Karpathos had vanished. We went inside to sit in the *salla* of Marigo Malliarakis; a chandelier, reactivated, glowed with a somber, unsteady light. Uncle George was sitting at the table, musing over photographs. My cousin and I sat beside him. Around us, Aphrodite hovered on silent feet. She would never sit with us: she pretended to be there on business, on some

° Turkish coins

imaginary errand. Now she was moving piles of letters from one table to another and back again.

"Come back to Kasos, have you?" she said. "You've taken your own advice and come here with your two nephews. But what you expect to find here I do not know. Whatever it is, you won't find it, and next week when the ship comes from Crete again and stops here on her way toward Rhodes, you'll sail away again. What do you want with a poor forsaken island, you and your nephews from England and America. But you take a poor old woman who had a life of her own in Alexandria, who had a boarding house where only English people stayed, and Arab servants who talked to her in Romaic and called her 'Madame Aphrodite,' and you tell her 'Go to Kasos. Stay in the old house. It is better for you.'"

"I never told you to go back. You wanted to."

"Yes, I wanted to come back. Of course I wanted to, because I thought it was Kasos I would be coming back to. I thought I would be coming back to the island I left on that day in 1899 when we all got on the ship for Syros: you, Basil, Nicholas, and Manuel, together with Captain Elias and my Eleni. When you told me, 'Go back to Kasos, stay in the old house,' how did I know there was no Kasos anymore? How did I know I was coming back to a heap of ashes?

"Better for me, you say? Yes, thank you very much. Better for me to shut myself up in my tomb so I won't have far to go when death comes for me. Better for me to lie down here and wait for them to come and take me on the sheet. Better for me, you say. Better for me? Maybe I'll go and throw myself in the sea. That would be better for me too."

"Now stop," my uncle said. "Is that your way to welcome us?"

"Oh, yes, I forgot. Welcome to you. Welcome to Kasos. Welcome to a Kasos that isn't here. This is not Kasos, so why should I welcome you? Kasos was here when the sky was all red in the west and it wasn't sunset. Kasos was here when the sky was all glowing over Crete and the hour was midnight. That was Kasos, when we all woke up at the peak of midnight because there was wailing and moaning in the town as though for death, and we went down to the Bucca and saw the sky all on fire over Crete with the flames of revolution. That was Kasos, when a boatload of Cretans sailed into the Bucca, and the five Turks who were living on the island went down to stop them, and they got as far as St. Spiridon and saw the Cretans with their swords and guns and they ran away and let them alone to sail away again for Karpathos. That was Kasos. Kasos was when the *Kaimakami** was living here in the last house of Phry where the road winds up hill to Ayia Marina, when he used to pass by this house on his way to meet the elders of the island, and when he used to walk under that balcony of our house, painted all light blue to go with our white walls for very spite of him, and when he used to call up, in Romaic, 'Good morning, Kyra Eleni.' And my Eleni would call down to him, in Romaic (just as I'm talking to you), 'Good-morning, Mr. Kaimakami.' "

At that moment, looking under the table, Aphrodite caught sight of my tape-recorder making its covert rotations.

"Christ and Virgin, will you look at that!" she said. "There is a genie listening to us! All the time we're talking, there's a demon underneath the table, listening to every word we say. Holy Virgin! As if we don't have enough trouble on this island, we have this nephew from America who brings a genie to catch our words! Now, will someone please tell me again: whose child is that?"

"Michael's," said my uncle. "My brother Michael's."

"Ah, yes, Michael's," Aphrodite said.

My cousin laughed at that, and Aphrodite looked at him as though seeing him for the first time.

"What are you laughing at, my boy? Do you understand what we are saying? George, do these children understand Romaic?"

* The Turkish governor of the island.

"Of course they do," my uncle said. "That one is writing a book, and he's brought his tape-recorder to listen to every word you say. And when he returns to America, he's going to write it all down, so the whole world can hear your foolishness."

"*Kyrie Eleison!*" said Aphrodite, making the sign of the cross. "Then I won't say anything. I'll be silent as the grave."

She was silent as the grave for one moment.

"Come back to Kasos, have you?" she continued. "Come back with your nephew and his demon. But there is no Kasos here. There is only this abandoned rock with its roofs fallen in and its houses empty. There are no people living here, only goats and donkeys. It's an island of asses you returned to. Not to Kasos, not the Kasos I have known. And you, my nephew from America, let me tell you something."

She turned to me now, her thick lenses flashing the light of the chandelier into my eyes.

"You, my son of Michael, if you had come to Kasos sixty years ago, you would have found it. If you had been in Kasos when your grandparents were newly married, then you would have seen it. Let me tell you about that Kasos."

So the muse sang to me of Kasos, of a Kasos that had been and was no more. She sang of fifty sailing ships anchored in the lee of Makra Island, of caiques plying the windy passage with seamen coming home. She sang of the grape harvest, and planting time in November, and the Karpathian women in their white robes and cowls come to Kasos to work in the fields. She sang of the feast days of the island saints, of violins, *laouts* and lyres, of the *sousta*, danced by young men and women in a line.

She sang of Palm Sunday, when everyone went to Church to get a cross of palms which was good protection from the "Evil Eye." Of Good Friday when the bell tolled at sundown and the elders carried the tomb of Christ through the streets, and twelve priests followed in their black robes of mourning, chanting solemnly. Of the island *lamentatrice* who wailed the dirges for the island's dead and that night wailed the saddest dirge of all, in a voice as piercing as a violin: "Where is there a ravine to hurl myself, where is there a sea to drown me. Where is there a razor to cut down my hair, a mother's hair whose Son is on the Cross."

"My son of Michael," she said to me, "on Holy Saturday, you would have been on the square before the church with everyone on Kasos, the island all quiet, with only the waves pounding in the darkness. Near midnight, you would have seen the priests come out in golden robes instead of black, one of them carrying the lighted candle, passing the light to the congregation. You would have seen the light handed on from candle to candle until the whole square was bright. And beyond the Bucca, you would have seen all the ships of Kasos come from Makra Island to stand at anchor in a line, their masts and rigging suddenly aglow with torches. You would have seen the island suddenly illumined, and you would have heard the joyful song of the Resurrection, 'Christ is Risen from the Dead.' You would have heard that song and sung it yourself, along with your grandfather and grandmother and all the natives of your island. You would have seen all the people returning to their houses, candles flickering on all the roads and in all the windows of the island. And you would have returned to this house with your grandmother and grandfather, still singing the song of Resurrection, 'Christ is risen from the dead.' And that was Kasos, my son of Michael, of the demon's ears. That was the Kasos you would have known, if you had not arrived too late."

Black Bird
Over
Kasos

*T*he island is like me, and the island's life is like my life. I went to Greece as an infant in 1939 and spent almost a year in Syros. Ever since, people have told me things that happened in that year: how I used to sit on the terrace outside the villa in the hills and pretend I was on the bridge of a sailing ship, how I used to ride on my grandfather's shoulders, how I spoke infant Greek in the heavy accents of the islands. But despite what people told me, I can remember nothing for myself. The first memory I have of life is still that hotel room and the arabesques on the carpet; and English is my only native language.

In the same way, in some remote era of the past, Kasos was a Hellenic island. But the island does not remember. It is separated from its own past, just as I am separated from my past. When the island awoke to memory, it knew nothing of its former life. The only Greece it could believe in was the Greece it knew: a subject people in a foreign nation. As far as Kasos could remember, it had been born in *xenitia*.

35

Greece itself—modern Greece—is a very young nation. People usually think of ancient Hellas, and they often do not realize that as a modern nation, Greece is younger than the United States. Greece was born in a revolution against the Turks in 1821. Its result was a fraction of present Greece: Peloponnesos, a small corridor of the mainland, and a few Aegean islands in the neighborhood of Syros. Many other lands and islands were left out of the new nation, including Kasos. For more than a century, Greece pursued her destiny, redeeming her lost children. In 1864, she acquired the Seven Islands of the Ionian; in 1881, Thessaly; in 1913, portions of Macedonia and Epirus, the islands of Samos, Chios, Lesbos, and others in the north Aegean. At last, in 1948, she redeemed the final islands: a group lying between Crete and Turkey, known as the Dodecanese, one of which is Kasos.

So Kasos became Greek in 1948. Since the founding of the Byzantine Empire in 330 A.D., it was ruled by Arabs, Venetians, Turks, Russians, Turks again, and finally Italians. With its neighbor Karpathos, it has been under non-Greek rule longer than any portion of present Greece. Since 1306, it has been Greek for nineteen years, from 1948 to the present. With the other islands of the Dodecanese, it is the youngest of Greece's children, the last to be redeemed.

The first people known to have stood on Kasos were Phoenicians. They gave the island its name: the island of sea-foam. The island is mentioned in the ship list of the Iliad—Hellenized as Kasos—along with other islands of the area. Later it was settled by the Dorians at about the time they settled Rhodes, Kos, and Crete, and from that time onward, Kasos fell under the administration of Rhodes, where it has remained.

During the classical period, the city of Kasos was on the site of the present town of Poli (the name itself means city) on a steep slope at the southeastern corner of the plateau. There, the German archeologist Ludwig Ross, arriving in 1847, found the remnants of an ancient wall and the fragments of a statue, probably of Apollo.

The ancient harbor Imborio (meaning trade or commerce) was exactly on the site of the present harbor, a small cove beneath the town of Panayia, where there was a shipbuilding yard up to the end of the nineteenth century. Because of its geographical position, Kasos must have done a fair trade, and like Rhodes and its other neighbors, it must have been densely populated.

By the end of the first century of the Christian era, Kasos was a part of the Roman Empire, like the rest of Greece, and in A.D. 330 when the Empire moved to Byzantium, Kasos came under the rule of the emperor on the Bosporus. According to tradition, the Bishop of Karpathos and Kasos (a seat which exists today) attended the first Ecumenical Council in Nicaea in A.D. 325. At that time, the island must still have been densely populated, as Ludwig Ross surmised from the number of Byzantine coins which he found.

But time, and ironically, the same geographical position which had helped it flourish was to take its toll on Kasos. In the seventh century, the dark wave of Islam curled northward out of Arabia, and by 828, it had broken over Kasos. Like its neighbors Crete and Karpathos, the island became an outpost for Arab pirates. In 961, the Byzantines reconquered it, but by that time the sun was setting on the Empire. In 1204, the knights of the Fourth Crusade turned from their stated destination, and instead of attacking the infidel at Jerusalem, they attacked the Emperor at Constantinople whom they considered a heretic, because of the schism of the churches in 1054. On that day, hated in the Romaic world forever after, the ancient city of Constantine was sacked. A western ruler, Baldwin of Flanders, was seated on the Byzantine throne, and the Romaic lands were divided among the western princes. The Byzantines retreated and put up a throne at Nicaea, and by 1261, they had rallied northward, expelled the western ruler, and captured Constantinople once again. In 1282, the Byzantine Emperor gave Kasos, Karpathos, and Crete to a Genoese "free-lance" named Andrea Moresco in return for his allegiance against the Venetians. By that time, the once populous island of Kasos, ransacked by centuries of Aegean pirates, must have become a poor rock, safe collateral for Moresco's far from certain loyalty. But Moresco had no time to prove his loyalty one way or another. He was taken prisoner in a campaign against Cyprus, and in his absence, the Knights of St. John under William of Villaret took the island of Rhodes, and in the same year, 1306, a Venetian named Andrea Cornaro° took Karpathos and Kasos. For the next two centuries, Kasos was held by the Cornaro family as a fief to Venice.

In the meantime, a darker day had dawned on the Empire. On a black Tuesday in 1453, the Ottoman Turks conquered the city on the Bosporus. A Sultan sat in the Emperor's throne and the people of the Empire were reduced to the status of a subject nation, known to their masters as *Romaioi,* their language as Romaic. The following decades were the heyday of the Turks, when they carried the crescent into Belgrade and Budapest, and even the princes of western Europe dreaded their invincible advance. Headed by the renowned pirate Barbarossa, the Ottoman fleet conquered most of the Archipelago. In 1522, the Knights of St. John were driven out of Rhodes and the adjacent islands, and fled the east forever, to Malta. By 1537, the Ottomans had taken most of the Archipelago, including Karpathos and Kasos. The Cornaro family were driven out and forced to take refuge in the remaining Venetian stronghold of Crete, and from that year onward, like most of Greece, Kasos became part of the Ottoman Empire.

The succeeding centuries brought little change to Kasos as they brought little change to Greece. The Turks and Venetians

° Probably an ancestor of the epic poet Vicenzo Cornaro.

waged a continual battle for the Romaic lands, but this battle made no difference to the Greeks. As a political people, the Greeks did not exist. They participated in the struggle only as galley-slaves, fighting on both sides, killing each other in the service of others. But those long centuries of Turkish rule were not hard on Kasos. Like the other rocks around it, the very poverty in Kasos saved it from the brunt of Turkish tyranny. Suleiman, the Sultan who conquered the Dodecanese, saw little purpose in ruling these barren places. Instead, he granted the islands certain privileges, later confirmed by successive Sultans through the nineteenth century. Except for Rhodes and Kos, which were fertile and populous enough to make a stricter rule worthwhile, these islands were to have no Turkish governors. Their citizens were not to be subject to induction in the Turkish armies, and their only obligation was to pay a yearly tax, according to their population. The islanders were to collect this tax—no Turkish officials were allowed to interfere—and in all other matters, the islanders were to rule themselves.

Because of these privileges, Kasos was able to develop a workable system of self-government. By the beginning of the nineteenth century, its main ruling body was a group of elders representing each of the villages, elected annually by the entire population of the island. This body, known as the *Demogerontia,* handled the collection of the tax and otherwise regulated the civil and commercial life of the island. Disputes were settled according to local customs which were unwritten but highly rigid, and interpreted always by the elders of the island. In addition, there was an ecclesiastical court to decide questions relating to dowry or inheritance and other spiritual matters. Finally there was a political court which tried minor criminal cases. (The few major crimes in the history of the island were tried in Rhodes.)

But however able Kasos was to rule itself, a rocky island with no shelter from the sea could offer little protection for its inhabitants. The islanders built their villages at the interior of the plateau, as far from the sea as possible, but throughout the fifteenth and sixteenth centuries, when piracy in the Aegean was at its height, Kasiot homes were never safe from plunder, and the Kasiots themselves were constantly being carried off to the slave markets of Asia Minor and North Africa. During these centuries, the population of the island was steadily depleted, until finally at the end of the sixteenth century, travelers passing by the island found it uninhabited.

In this period, Kasos was actually severed from its past. Bald and solitary as an infant, it was carried mindlessly upon the sea. During that time, it was probably re-settled by Albanians. A village at the interior of the plateau named Arvanitohori (Albanian-Town) was founded, according to a tradition Ludwig Ross heard in 1847, by an Albanian brigand from the island of Syros. In addition, there must have been non-Albanians living on Kasos at the time, probably Cretans fleeing the persecution of both Venetians and Turks. (Otherwise why should Albanians themselves name it Albanian-Town?)

In the meantime, the mind of Kasos slept on, not remembering. During this era, no light fell upon the island, just as before the dawn of memory, no light fell upon the infant's mind. In those dark and uninhabited decades, Kasos was a phantom island, buoyed upon an unremembered sea. The miracle is that when it emerged at last, Kasos was Greek: the miracle of heredity itself. Not only is there no Albanian spoken on Kasos today, in Arvanitohori or any other village, but none of the languages of its other erstwhile masters is spoken either: no Turkish, Arabic, or Italian, except those elements that have been assimilated into Greek. In addition, there are other strong traces of the island's Hellenism, preserved unconsciously. They are implicit in naming and inheritance customs, in rites of grieving, in a cult of vengeance, in casual references to Charon, the Fates, and other pagan deities heard in Kasos to this day. These are not memories of the island's former life, for the island itself does not remember. But they are unconscious re-enactments of it, just as an adult's life is an unconscious re-enactment of what he has experienced as an infant. If Kasos could remember, it would remember its Hellenic past, just as, if the human mind could be unlocked so that a person could remember events that happened to him at the age of two, I would find myself revealed at last, on my grandfather's shoulders, speaking Greek.

Then, toward the end of the eighteenth century the island awakened. Suddenly, in 1788, a light was thrown upon it, and the island was revealed.

The French philosopher Claude Savary, bound for Crete, met adverse winds and was forced to seek refuge on a barren island thirty miles from his destination. He spent about a week there, waiting for calmer weather, and during that time he wrote a letter describing his accidental visit, included in his volume *Letters on Greece*, published in 1788.

"The boat was let down," he wrote, "but we knew not where to land. All over the coast we could discover nothing but threatening, pointed rocks against which the waves broke with a bellowing noise, whitening them with foam."

Here indeed was the island of the Phoenicians. One of the inhabitants came down to the shore and waved a handkerchief near a place where Savary could land. It was the Bucca, which exists today: a small harbor, sealed off from the sea by two breakwaters. Today the Bucca is surrounded by the town of Phry, a placid bowl beneath the belltower with the clock. But in those days there was no town and no belltower. Phry was built in the 1830's to house the refugees returning to Kasos after the Revolution. But in 1788, the plain around the Bucca was bare. On the plateau above, four Kasiot villages peered at the approaching strangers.

But the French flag flying in the lee of Makra Island must have relieved the Kasiots. Trusting these men approaching the

Bucca, the anonymous Kasiot came down to meet them, not realizing quite another possibility: that this was not a piratical but a historical adventure. Waving his handkerchief in all ingenuousness, he beckoned the discoverer to wrest his island from secure oblivion.

The entrance to the Bucca was no more than a dozen feet wide, no wider than it is today. To enter it, the boat must proceed cautiously, through the middle of the opening, with no room around it even for the oars to be extended. As Savary's boat advanced, a violent surge rose suddenly, threatening to dash the boat against the rocks. The Kasiot called one of his countrymen, and the two of them came up, one on either side of the opening, signaling to Savary's men to push forward with the oars. At the instant the boat entered the treacherous pass, they held it off with long poles and guided it into the harbor.

In that way, Kasos was discovered. In the person of this lucky Frenchman, Kasos made connection with its future. For the first time in history, a recording eye was turned upon the island, remembering what it saw. And now, from Savary's description, we see an island we can recognize.

Below the hill from which I made my observations, stands a small chapel surrounded by fig-trees. Here begin a chain of hills that, bending into a semi-circle, leave in the middle a plain of a league in circumference, which has been cleared out by the inhabitants, with infinite labor. They have torn up large pieces of rock, and removed heaps of stones, with which they have formed the walls of the inclosure. All this space is divided into compartments and shared among the Kasiots. They sow barley and wheat . . . The sides of the hills are covered with vineyards, the grapes of which produce a very agreeable wine. I could not help admiring the industry with which these islanders have been able to cultivate rocks, hardly covered with a few inches of earth . . .

Savary noticed, as one would notice today, that the inhabitants of the island were mostly women and old men. The young men sowed their fields in October and November (the only months when there is rain on Kasos even now). They stayed at home until the crops were harvested in March. Then soon afterward, they went to sea, to trade in the Archipelago.

For dinner that evening, Savary ate pullet with rice, fresh eggs, pigeons, cheese, and wine. He found the eating habits different from Paris; the men dining by themselves, in a circle on the carpet, the women in a separate room. After dinner, there was a dance.

About twenty young girls, dressed all in white, with flowing robes, and plaited locks, entered the apartment, and with them a young man who played on the lyre, which he accompanied with his voice. Several of them were handsome, all healthy and lively . . . The uniform dress of these nymphs, the modesty which heightened their charms, their becoming bashfulness, their joyous but decent merriment, all contributed to make me almost imagine myself suddenly transported to the island of Calypso. They began to range themselves in a ring, and invited me to dance. I did not wait for many entreaties. The circle we formed is singular from the manner in which it is interwoven: the dancer does not give his hand to the two persons next him, but to those next them, so that you can have your hands crossed before your neighbors, who are thus locked, as it were, in the links of a double chain. This interweaving is not without pleasure, for reasons by no means difficult to understand. In the middle of the circle stood the musician, who played and sang at the same time, while all the dancers kept exact time . . . For myself, I followed where my partners led me, my mind being less occupied with the dance than with the charming females who composed it."*

* The dance was the *Foumisto*, traditionally danced at weddings, but apparently also on special occasions such as the arrival of a Frenchman.

Savary's host, anxious for him to take away a good report of the island, showed him letters written by two Provençal captains landed on Kasos before him. The Kasiot could not read French, but he knew they must be testimonials to his native island, and valuing them among his most precious possessions, he kept them locked up in a coffer. Proudly, he brought them out and unrolled them for Savary.

The first one read: "Frenchmen, whom the tempest may throw upon this island, confide in the inhabitants: I was shipwrecked on these rocks, and they afforded me every succour that men owe each other in similar misfortunes."

The second one read: "I warn such of my countrymen as chance may bring [to Kasos] to be upon their guard and put no confidence in the inhabitants. They are a set of thieves and knaves and strangers have everything to apprehend from their rapacity."

Looking up at his host, Savary saw him beaming with pleasure, and so he returned the letters to him, saying only that he needed no testimonials to rely on his integrity. The Kasiot smiled in great satisfaction and locked up his treasure once again.

For his part, Savary did well by Kasos. He was a Frenchman in the tradition of Rousseau, and what he found on Kasos suited him.

Happy people, ambition and intrigue trouble not your tranquillity; the thirst of gold hath not corrupted your manners; the quarrels, dissensions, and crimes with which it hath covered the earth are to you unknown. Here, no citizen, proud of his titles, or his wealth, tramples under foot his humble countrymen; no cringing valet flatters the vices of his master; man is equal to man, nor does the Kasiot blush, or abase himself before the Kasiot.

Before the passing of that generation, the Greek Revolution had broken out. Actually, the Kasiots had very little to gain from it, since they already possessed almost complete freedom. But freedom meant not only deliverance from oppression but national identity. Ever since 1821, no Greek considered himself free unless his land were part of Greece. If he lived beyond the boundaries of the nation, he considered himself "unredeemed," and what he called the cause of freedom was identical with the cause of *Enosis*, or union with his mother Greece. For that reason, however free from oppression the Kasiots may have been in 1821, they were as eager to raise the flag of revolution as though they had been suffering under the tyrant's heel.

In 1770, the Russian fleet had occupied the Archipelago in an abortive campaign against the Turks. In the brief period of their tenure, the Russians taught the Greek islanders seamanship and naval warfare. During the Napoleonic Wars, the increased trade in the Mediterranean enabled several Greek islands to develop powerful merchant fleets: Hydra, Spetsai, Psara, and Kasos. When the Revolution broke out, this merchant marine was transformed into a navy, which was to a large extent responsible for the success of the Revolution.

A Kasiot captain, Grigoriades, was on his way from Smyrna to Syros with Moslem passengers on board when news of the Revolution reached him. Suddenly, he changed course and sailed for Kasos. There, anchoring in full view of the Kasiot population, he brought all the Moslem passengers on deck and cut their throats. As he declared boastfully sometime later, he wanted to share Moslem blood with Kasos, to stain it indelibly with revolution, to bind its destiny irrevocably with the destiny of Greece.

But the Kasiots did not need such a spectacle to stir them. Immediately, they put to sea, armed with guns and ammunition bought or stolen from neutral ships. At home, a population of

3,500 prepared for war. At the time, the Hydriots had a hundred and fifteen ships over a hundred tons, the Spetsiots sixty, the Psariots forty, and the Kasiots fifteen. When the Greek revolutionaries formed a central treasury and began to levy taxes, the Hydriots, as the largest naval power, were authorized to make the collections and dispense the proceeds. In effect, they assumed command over Greek naval operations. For some reason lost to history, the Hydriots decided that the Kasiots should not be full-fledged members of the Revolutionary navy. If the Kasiots wished to sail with the ships of the other three naval islands, they must do so not with funds drawn from the central treasury but at their own expense. The Kasiots did so, for a time. Then, later, fearing an attack upon their island, which was more distant from the mainland and more exposed to the enemy than Hydra and Spetsai, they returned to protect it.

Thereafter, the Kasiots acted on their own. Their main area of operations was off the coasts of Crete and in southeastern part of the Mediterranean. When the Cretan population rose, the Kasiot ships assisted in the sieges of the fortresses along the northern shore: Khania, Suda, and Rethymnon. In the meantime, they also set up a blockade of the island, harassing the Turkish supply lines by intercepting many ships, including those of neutral powers, with cargoes intended for the Turks. In addition, they raided the islands of Kos, Rhodes, Cyprus, and even as far as the coasts of Karamania, Syria, and Egypt. In Damietta, four Kasiot captains surprised thirteen vessels loaded with rice for the Sultan's fleet, one of them containing one million piastres in cash. Seizing three of the ships, they filled them with the piastres and as much more booty as they would hold, and towed them off for Kasos.

The Sultan could not bear such outrages for long. By the beginning of 1823, Greek fortunes were ebbing. The Sultan's Egyptian viceroy, Mohammed Ali, entered the war and sent his son, Ibrahim Pasha, to put down the revolt in Crete. By the beginning of 1824, the fires in Crete had been reduced to embers. Much of the population had fled the island, mostly in Kasiot ships; and an estimated 2,500 had taken refuge in Kasos. Now, in 1824, Ibrahim's next step was to be Peloponnesos itself. Before embarking on such an invasion, he must have a base in Crete and secure supply lines from Egypt. And for this purpose, he must put an end to the power of a barren island, thirty miles off Crete's eastern tip. So the beginning of 1824 boded ominously for Kasos.

The Kasiots wrote to Hydra, begging for the fleet to come to their assistance. Their appeal was not only in their own interests, but in the interests of Greece. If they could resist Ibrahim's invasion, the Egyptians' entire northward offensive would be delayed. But the Kasiots were to be snubbed again by Hydra. The Hydriots replied that the sailors would not put to sea without wages, and therefore they could not dispatch the fleet until a loan arrived from England. Again, the Hydriot motives are unknown. Even without the loan from England, there must have been plenty of money in the Hydriot treasury and true patriots will sail without wages if necessary. Probably, the Hydriots were too occupied with the feuding then going on among the Greek leaders to perceive the danger. That internecine strife proved tragic, costing many lives not only in Kasos but in Psara, Mesolonghi, and other Greek strongholds.

So Kasos was left alone with her destiny. The captains could have transported the population to mainland Greece, just as they had transported many Cretans during the previous year. But they felt they must defend their homes in the face of danger. They believed their surest chance against the overwhelming odds would be to make their defense on land. The iron-bound coast of Kasos afforded no easy access, and they believed if they could fortify the three miles across the opening of the plateau, the rest of the island would defend itself. Accordingly, they disarmed their ships and anchored them at Imborio. With a total of some thirty guns, they erected a battery across the mouth of the plateau, spaced out behind a rampart extending from Imborio in the east to St. George of the Spring in the west.

Behind the rampart, five hundred Kasiots took their places with five hundred Cretans. Behind them, in the four villages that had peered down at Savary, an unarmed population grown to 5,000 waited in their houses.

There are two conflicting versions of what happened. Both agree that the Egyptian fleet appeared under forty-five sail, led by an ex-pirate Ismael Gibraltar, transporting a troop of three to four thousand Albanians under the command of Hussein Bey. Both agree that the Egyptians tried one unsuccessful assault, sailed away, and returned on the night of June 19 (June 7 according to the old calendar). But they offer widely different explanations of what happened next.

The first version is a Kasiot tradition. Ludwig Ross heard it in 1847, and when I arrived in 1964, it was still there. According to this version, the Egyptians opened fire on their first attack; and unable to bring the island to submission, they steered directly for the open land at the opening of the plateau and attempted an invasion. But Kasiot resistance proved too strong for them. Against overwhelming odds, the rampart held. Shamefully repulsed, the Egyptians gave way and sailed off for Rhodes. And there, to the island's everlasting grief, they found a Kasiot named Zacharias, exiled from his native island for immoral behavior. On the night of June 19/7, he returned to Kasos with the Egyptian fleet, and—compounding immorality with treason—he showed them a secret cleft in the iron coast, a fatal landing place beyond the range of the thirty guns.

The second version comes from Alexandria, in an anonymous letter to the British Ambassador at Constantinople. Since it comes originally from Egypt, it must be the version the fleet brought home. According to this report, as the Egyptian warships advanced upon the island, the flagship *Diana*—struck a reef, opening a large hole in her side. Shipping water rapidly, the *Diana* turned from battle; thinking she was leading a retreat, the other Egyptian warships turned from battle after her. Then the fleet sailed away to repair the damage, in the direction of Rhodes. They found a harbor, probably in Karpathos, and anchored there until the *Diana* could repair the damage. Then, this work done, they returned to Kasos and sacked the island.

I confess I incline to the second version. It seems unbelievable that the Egyptians could have found a Kasiot exile among the population of Rhodes. How would he have made his way to them? How would he have known their naval strategy—that they were planning an attack on Kasos—and so come down to volunteer his services? According to the legend, Zacharias killed himself during the invasion, but his body was not found afterward by the surviving population, as it surely would have been to be decorated in ways appropriate to a traitor. Finally, the secret cleft in the Kasiot coast could not have been a secret. It was a strip of beach called *Antiperatos,* which exists today just west of where the rampart would have ended. We saw it on our arrival in 1964, and the Egyptians must have seen it when they approached the island from the same direction. They must have seen the town of Ayia Marina on the hill above it, and for that reason, the Kasiot defenses must have seemed naïve to them: a rampart studiously guarding the mouth of the plateau, when beyond it lay an unprotected landing site.

But although the Kasiot defenses did not prove invincible, the Kasiot imagination did. It was not the first time in history that outnumbered Greeks have held out against the enemy until betrayed by treachery. The Spartans at Thermopylae held the pass against overwhelming odds, until a traitor showed the enemy a secret cleft between the mountains. More than two thousand years later, the story of the fall of Kasos is so similar, it seems likely that the Kasiots who survived that night simply used it to explain the failure of their defenses. Remembering the

Spartans, they fitted the ancient story to the present facts. They gave their traitor a name and a motive (which was better than the Spartans could do at Thermopylae). Then, after his work was done, they disposed of him by his own hand.

But except for Zacharias, the versions of the Egyptian landing are in agreement. June 19/7 was a dark night. Anchoring off Kasos a second time, the Egyptians sent eighteen landing craft in an apparent attempt to land before the thirty guns. This landing was only a diversionary maneuver, and while it occupied the Kasiots' attention, thirty more landing craft crept up the shore to Antiperatos, the sandy beach beyond the guns. There the invaders surprised four Kasiots guards and slew them without a sound. And from then on, the island's doom was sealed. Soundlessly, three thousand Albanians crept up the slope to Ayia Marina and took instant possession of the village. From that point, the highest habitable vantage point, they must have seen exactly the same sight Savary had described four decades earlier: a plateau of a league in circumference, with three more villages lying before them. Now the Kasiots at the rampart, their guns pointing in the wrong direction, could be taken from the rear. Hussein hoped to take as many prisoners as possible, to impress them into service on Ismael's ships; and before attacking, he made his presence known and gave the Kasiots a chance to surrender. In that interval, some Kasiots hid in caves and others escaped in small boats, sailing miraculously through the Egyptian fleet, eventually to find refuge on other islands. But at last, Hussein's patience was at an end. The remaining Kasiots refused his offer, and he unleashed the Albanians.

Burning and pillaging, they laid waste the island. They killed a total of five hundred Kasiots and Cretans, impressed the rest as sailors in the Egyptian navy, and took two thousand Kasiot women and children slaves to be sold in the markets of Smyrna and Alexandria. They burned all the ships standing on the ways, and towed the fifteen ships anchored at Imborio back to Crete.

When the Hydriots arrived at last—after the enemy had gone on
to destroy Psara—they found a ghost of Kasos. The island was
deserted; skeletons of houses stared at their arrival; and the only
visible sign of life was a black bird, making circles overhead.

But the treachery of fortune was not yet over. From that time
onward, Kasos performed no service for the Revolution. It had
lost its people to *xenitia,* some to destitution on other islands,
others to a harsher fate in the slave marts of Smyrna and Alexandria. The island itself was as barren as it had been in the
sixteenth century. But in the meantime, the Greek Revolution
had come to its successful end. In 1827, in Navarino Bay, the
united ships of the English, French, and Russians, destroyed the
Turkish fleet. In a treaty of 1829, a new nation came into existence.

The only problem, from Kasos' point of view, was that it was
not included in this nation. It was made part of the first agreement of 1829, but then in an afterthought, in the London
Protocol of 1830, it was left out. By a correction made in a London conference room, the island of Euboea which had been
Turkish was awarded to Greece, and Kasos and the rest of the
Dodecanese, which had been Greek, were returned to Turkey.

The island itself had a false arrival. As other Greek lands and
islands arrived at their journey's end—Syros among them—
Kasos reached a way-station, a vantage point from which another
journey extended, to a future which could only be imagined
beyond a remaining expanse of time and sea.

What's in a Name?

A name is a paradox. A name is what a person is, but it is the one thing he cannot decide. Our names are the titles that other people give to our existence, and we are all what we are—George, Michael, Elias—not by our choice but by the workings of some whimsy that is not our own.

In Kasos, even parents are not free to choose their children's names. Instead, by Kasiot custom, the name itself chooses the infant. I am Elias because I am the first son of my father, and because my father is the son of a first son, and my father's father was also the first son of a first son, and that original first son, the one who precedes all the rest and antedates my own arrival by almost a hundred and fifty years, was also Elias Kulukundis.

That first Elias, who wore a fez and baggy trousers, is the first Kulukundis of record. Like the founder of any family, his life has become a legend among his descendants. The first we hear of him, he was on Kasos in 1824. After the destruction of the island, he made his way to Amorgos. There he met a Kasiot

55

girl taking refuge with her family: Annezio Mavrandonis. Soon he married her and in 1827, the year of Navarino, she bore him his first son.

The custom is honored all over Greece, not only Kasos, that the first son be named for the father's father. Old Elias made no exception: he named his first son George, for his father. And when this second George became a father, his own first-born was Elias again, for *his* father. That second Elias was Captain Elias who shared the house of the blue shutters with his wife Eleni. When Eleni bore him a son, that latest first-born was named George again: Uncle George of the bananas and plaster cats. And when Uncle George became a father in London, his own first-born was Elias again, nicknamed Eddie.

In Kasos, the second son is named for the mother's father. Thereafter, the sons are named for the brothers of the parents, the third son for the father's eldest brother, the fourth for the mother's, the fifth for the father's next eldest brother, sixth for the mother's.°

The daughters follow the same pattern, in reverse. The first-daughter is named for the mother's mother, the second for the father's, the third for the mother's eldest sister, and so on. My family tree provides numerous examples of the male naming patterns,° but few of the female. That is because the old Kulukundis fathers were very good at getting their way in the lottery of the genders, and sons were always preferred.

"How many children do you have?" someone might ask a Kasiot father.

"Four," the father might reply, "four children, and two daughters."

My father has four surviving brothers and no sister; and in the succeeding generation, there are ten males and three females. Of those three, two were born at once. Twin girls were born to my Aunt Maro, Uncle Nicholas' wife, in London in

° See genealogy.

1935. The first was named Maryellie after her mother's mother; the second, her junior by fifteen minutes, Eleni.

The naming customs relate directly to inheritance codes. A parent was free to pass on all property acquired in his lifetime according to his will, and he would usually distribute it equally among all his children. But whatever property the parent had in turn inherited himself—his *ancestral* property—had to follow a code which was parallel to the naming customs. By this code, a first son inherited all his father's ancestral property, in other words, the property ultimately of his father's father, whose name he bore. Similarly, a first daughter would inherit all her mother's ancestral property, including her mother's house. (Houses in Kasos were owned maternally.)

Though unwritten, these customs had the force of law. Any conflicts were settled in the ecclesiastical court of the island, always in accordance with the custom. Even if one party was resident in Greece and appealed to a contrary provision of Greek law, Kasiot custom would take precedence. The Greek government decided that while populations such as the Kasiots remained under Ottoman rule, their local customs must be protected as the main bulwark of their autonomy. Until 1948, when Kasos and the rest of the Dodecanese became part of Greece, the dictum was respected by both Greek and Turkish courts that "local custom is the law."*

How the customs came about is a matter of speculation. Some scholars contend they are remnants of feudal law introduced into the islands by the Venetians. Others observe that the customs do not exist in Peloponnesos and mainland Greece, areas which were also settled by Venetians, only on Kasos and certain other islands. Instead, according to these other scholars, the customs must be older than the Venetians and probably originated in the religion of the ancients. In ancient Greece, a

---

* Since then the island has been subject to Greek law, though the customs are still tacitly observed for sentimental reasons.

first son was also named for his father's father. After the father's death, this first son would tend his grave and perform services in ministration for his soul. For this reason, by religious precept, the son would acquire the land adjacent to his father's grave, which would then become his ancestral property, to be handed on to his own first son.

But a set of customs may originate for certain reasons and be preserved for totally different ones. Like any custom, this naming and inheritance code had the practical effect of removing the necessity of human choice. Unconsciously, parents might actually come to favor those children named for their side of the family, and in this way, affection could be divided equitably. Naturally, one would have to look far beneath the surface of any family to observe such preferences, but sometimes they became apparent. Eleni's second son, Basil, died at thirteen. When he died, his grandmother, Old Yia-Yia, seized his brother Nicholas by the throat and said, "Why didn't you die instead of Basil?" Little Nicholas was bewildered. "Why should I die instead of Basil?" he said. And what poor Nicholas was far from guessing was that in her frenzy, Old Yia-Yia was admitting that she considered Basil *her* grandson in a way Nicholas could never be: Basil was named for her late husband, Vasilios Mavroleon, whereas Nicholas was named, not for anyone in her family, but for his father's eldest brother.

Human choice would be even more divisive in the question of inheritance. Without a house, a Kasiot girl could not marry. Only a wealthy man could afford to build houses for several daughters, but in any family, there was already at least one house, the mother's. Without the custom, the family would find it very difficult to decide which daughter should have it. What mortal could confer the joys of wedlock on one girl and deny them to another? Instead, the question was left to custom to decide: the first daughter would have the house, and afterward, all her unmarriageable sisters could live with her, like my aunts in Syros, as a retinue of attendant maidens. Bearing no grudge, either against their elder sister or their parents, they would embrace their fate of fealty. The elder sister did not seek the privilege, and her parents did not confer it on her. It simply fell to her in the way the universe was ordered, by an inexorable tradition, according to the lottery of birth.

But the names are more than a custom; they are a manifestation of eternity. The child is not simply named for his grandfather. He *is* the grandfather incarnate. In the person of the child, the elder relatives see the grandfather before them.

"The eyes," says one.

"The mouth," another.

"The forehead," a third, in chorus.

"Captain Stathi!" called my aunts in Syros to a bewildered boy of twelve in a T-shirt with Latin characters spelling RYE across his chest. In those aged women's minds, this boy was Captain Stathi, their niece's husband, who built the villa in the hills and died there in 1942.

Stathi is Captain Stathi, I am Captain Elias, and my cousin Eleni, the younger twin, a young American woman who teaches remedial reading on New York's Lower East Side, is the mistress of the house of the blue shutters. We are all our grandparents, to those black-cowled seers of the island.

We have a painting of Old Elias, in his fez and tunic. Beside this painting we could place my cousin Eddie, who of all of us reincarnates his great-great-grandfather most precisely. We could imitate the black-cowled seers and say, isn't there a likeness between them? But actually, they are not alike at all. Even the black-cowled seers would know that, even if they called out, "The eyes, the mouth, the forehead!" Likeness *is* a question of eyes and foreheads and in those respects they are not alike. But they are identical, this unlike pair. There is an identity they share, impervious to time and travel which made them unalike in dress and speech. They have the same name; they are both Elias George Kulukundis.

The second Elias identifies the first one, for as long as there was an Elias George in London in 1932, then five generations earlier we could assume another one. And the first one in turn foretells the second, for as long as there was a first Elias George in Kasos in 1824, five generations later, wherever he might find himself, there must be another. That, of course, is providing that in the incubus of those successive generations, the seeds of the first-borns would endure, providing that there would be three first-born sons to span the intervening time, each one filling his portion of the hiatus. In that sense, the equation stretches further even than birth or death. The two Eliases do not postdate or antedate each other except in time, which is irrelevant. (The identity they share transcends both conception and demise.) As each time-imprisoned father, each poor impassioned George Elias or Elias George, performed his rhythm of paternity, there must have been a song of generations sounding in his ears, a song to sing a coming son, coaxing him to conception from the void. In that insistent relation of conceiver to conceived, the father began not to know if he was the father or the son, began not to know who was coming and who would come, until finally as the rhythm increased and the song was deepened, father and son had both escaped, leapt out of time so that each one of them was both father and son, in a relation to each other not of paternity but of identity. Now, as the space between them widened and receded, they became not son-father and father-son but grandfather-grandson and grandson-grandfather, withdrawing outward, returning inward once again, until finally at the climax both of the rhythm and the song, they were just one Elias singing in a timeless silence, singing what started as a song of generations and became the music of eternity, a song which has no beginning and no end and goes as follows: Elias George, George Elias, Elias George, George Elias George Elias George Elias George.

If Old Elias was a Cretan . . .

Some people believe that the development of any man re-
produces the entire history of the race. In that sense, the first
five years of my life reproduced the first twenty-five years of
Old Elias' life. At that time, last names were not in use in
Kasos. People were known as someone's son or daughter, and
Old Elias himself was known simply as Elias of George. Sometime after 1830, Old Elias sailed north to Syros, recently become a part of Greece, to register his ship with the Greek
authorities and gain the right to sail under the Greek flag. When
he arrived at the port authority, the harbormaster asked him his
name; and he replied, with the unthinking certitude of the
provincial: "Elias of George."

"Elias of George?" replied the harbormaster. "But that is not
enough. You must have some other name."

And so, poor Elias, remembering, was covered with embarrassment, and replied, blushingly, "If you like, they call me
Kulukundis."

That started all the trouble we have had with Kulukundis
ever since, all the spelling and correcting, and wondering and
disputing, not how but *why* we ever came by such a name.
I must have been five when I discovered it. Then I performed a
journey of my own, which in its way reproduced that ancient
journey of Old Elias the Fez when he first sailed up to Syros.
I was not dressed as a Greek islander, but in short flannel
trousers which I was ashamed to wear because I had bony legs.
And I wore no red fez but a short-peaked Eton cap, which I
hated passionately and took off and stuffed into my pocket as
soon as my parents were out of sight. Embarked on a mission
as awesome to me as that rude provincial's first arrival in the
metropolis of Syros, I set out in my father's car and journeyed
two miles to the metropolis of Rye. There, at the gate of a two-

story wooden building which housed two years of kindergarten and the first grade, I embarked on my first day in school.

"Your name?" said a tall woman, looking down at me.

"Elias," I said.

"Elias?" she said. "But you have another name. We have last names too."

If only I had known. If only the child could know that he is rehearsing the entire history of the race. If I had known of that other Elias five generations earlier, would I have stood straight and tall as though I were not wearing short pants but the silken baggy blue trousers of the Aegean islands? And would my Eton cap not have been stuffed away into my pocket, but on top of my head? For wasn't Old Elias' fez a curiosity in the westernized and cosmopolitan city of Syros, and had Old Elias taken it off and stuffed it into his pocket? No, I should have worn my Eton cap as proudly as though it were the emblem of service in a patriotic war. I might even have tipped it back a little as I drawled my reply, giving that kindergarten teacher an ancient comeback:

"If you like, they call me Kulukundis."*

Most Greek surnames are as long as Kulukundis, but they usually fall into certain categories. First, there are those derived from Christian names, with an ending—*poulos, akis, ides*—to denote paternity: Nikolakis is the son of Nicholas; Phillipides the son of Phillip. There are other names derived from towns or regions with *tis* added to signify the place of origin: Halkitis is the man from Halki; Roditis the man from Rhodes. There are names derived from trades: Kazantzis is the cauldron-maker (Kazantzakis, the son of the cauldron maker). Finally, there

* Once my father introduced himself to a Spaniard, and the man misheard the first two syllables, mistaking them for a vulgar word. (The same word exists in Greek.)

"*Kolo*kundis?" said the Spaniard. "Is that your name? Good God, let me change it for you. I'm a lawyer and I'll do it for nothing."

are names derived from nicknames: Kakoyanis is Bad John; Yeroyioryis, Strong George.

But the trouble with Kulukundis is that it doesn't fall into any of these categories, not at first glance. That was the final outrage, when I went to Greece at the age of seventeen. After carrying that curiosity through my childhood like an albatross around my neck, I thought finally I was in a country where people would accept it without a blink. But they didn't. The name is just as bizarre in Greek.

"Kulukundis," I said to a ground hostess who wanted to write my name on an airline ticket, and she looked up at me like any Spaniard. So if the name is not intelligible in the Athens airport, its meaning must be buried further back.

A professor at Athens University once made a list of Kasiot names and explanations of their origins.

"Kulukundis derives from the same stem as Kolokotronis," he declared, bringing my family dark amusement. Kolokotronis, hero of the Greek Revolution, derives his name from the *kolo* (the posterior region of the body which aroused our Spanish friend) and *kotrona,* which means boulder (the hero used to sit on boulders as he drew his battle plans). So Kulukundis may derive from the same stem as Kolokotronis, but what is the stem? All we have in common with the hero is the *kolo.**

So the troublesome question remains. Two of my uncles have presumed that for Old Elias to have withheld the name at first, then disclosed it blushingly, the name must originally have been a nickname; and each Uncle has reconstructed Old Elias' early history in such a way as to determine the meaning of this nickname.

The first is my Uncle Manuel, Eleni's fourth son. He heard from his Uncle Martis, who was a son of Old Elias himself, that the old man was taken prisoner by the Egyptians at the time of

* Actually, the theory has an obvious flaw: as I have observed more often than I care to remember, our name is spelled *Kulu* . . .

the sack of Kasos and put to work as a slave sailor on one of their ships of war.

"Before we begin," Uncle Manuel cautioned me, "I want you to remember that I am an historian with a flavor, so what I tell will not only be true, but it will have a little romance to it as well."

We were sitting in his drawing room, eleven floors above Central Park. We had just finished a Kasiot meal, which Uncle Manuel had prepared himself, moving back and forth from the conversation to the kitchen in serene preoccupation with his art. Now, he emerged with two cigars, and sat down to give flavor to my history.

"Imagine a young man about your age," he said. "A slave sailor on an Egyptian ship."

And so, Uncle Manuel, the muse of flavor, told of Old Elias' exploits as he had heard of them years before from his own uncle, handing on the knowledge as before, not from father to son but from uncle to nephew.

He told of an Aegean evening, sometime in 1826. A ship-of-war was sailing toward an island, lying like a shadow against the pink sky.

Like most sailing ships, this one had no latrine: the men used to retire and stand discreetly above the bowsprit. And so, as the ship neared the darkened island, no one thought it unusual when a young man went forward to stand in the cover of the dark. No one noticed a large bulge under the man's blue tunic. No one saw him take out a sheep's bladder used to carry wine or water but intended this evening for a different use. Cautiously, the young man inflated it, breathing silently through the neck. When the bladder was inflated to bizarre proportions, the young man clasped it to his chest, and as the ship verged toward the shadow island slipping by, he let himself into the sea.

"On that island," Uncle Manuel said, "a girl was waiting, the girl he eventually would marry."

The island, of course, was Amorgos, in the southern Cyclades, where an Egyptian ship might have been sailing in the spring of 1826, and where a certain Elias of George (of the bladder, should we call him now?), arrived to marry Annezio Mavrandonis and father a child to be born the next year, 1827, the year of Navarino.

In the two years between the sack of Kasos in 1824 and his marriage to Annezio Mavrandonis in 1826, Uncle Manuel reasoned Old Elias must have got his name. According to Uncle Martis, Old Elias was very tall and agile. There were Austrian officers aboard the warship, acting as advisors to the Egyptians, and they used to amuse themselves by devising contests to pit the Arab sailors against the Christian slaves. In one of these games, the officers would throw coins into the air, and let the Greeks and Arabs jump to catch them.

That is all Old Elias reported to his son. Uncle Martis surmised that Old Elias must have been running a sort of interference, blocking Egyptians out of the way so that his fellow Greeks could catch the coins. Thus, he earned an epithet from his compatriots: the coolie, for in blocking the opponents, he was pushing like a coolie. From *coolie*, Uncle Martis thought, he became Kulukundis.

At that point, Uncle Manuel parted company with Uncle Martis. The explanation did not satisfy him, and why should it, since it was not only specious but implausible? I see how one could become a coolie from Kulukundis (in fact, it has been done many times, as I and my brothers can testify from schooldays in Rye). But how you become Kulukundis from coolie is more difficult to see. What about all those other letters we all must spell out forever? If we are derived from a coolie, how did we come by all our extra baggage?

If Old Elias were tall and agile, Uncle Manuel reasoned, why would he be in the role of interference, blocking out the opposition? As the coach of any sport is well aware, you do not keep your tall and agile fellow for a blocker. You put him where he can catch things, a forward pass if that is your game, or in this case, the coins. Uncle Manuel reasoned that instead of blocking out the opposition, Old Elias was catching the coins himself. And since he was so tall and agile, in the two years he spent on board the ship, he must have caught a great many coins.

"So I thought to myself," said Uncle Manuel, "how would you say the one who gets the coins, or the one who gets everything, something like that? And I thought of all the possible things the Greek sailors might have called him, but I couldn't think of anything that sounded like Kulukundis. And then I remembered that in Arabic, the way you say all or everything is *kulu*. And then I found the answer! It wasn't the Greek sailors who gave him his name, but the Egyptians! I was looking for the answer in the wrong language. So I asked an Egyptian friend, 'How do you say: you get everything?' And my friend said, 'You can't say it that way in Arabic, you must put it a different way. You must say: everything comes to you.' 'And how would you say that?' '*Kulu enta*,' he said."

And there it is, the origin of the name, according to Uncle Manuel. "*Kulu enta*," the Egyptian sailors called out to Old Elias as he caught the coins, "Everything to you!" The Greeks heard that so often that they adopted it themselves, making it Greek. They heard *kulu enta* and they made it Kulukundis.

"*Kulu enta*, Kulukundis," Uncle Manuel was saying, but I could see something tantalizing him even then, perhaps the discrepancy between the two, persisting despite his ingenuity. And yet, bravely, he affirmed his theory: the origin of Kulukundis is *kulu enta*, the one who gets everything, the one to whom all things come.[*]

Sitting in Uncle Manuel's armchair, enjoying his cigar, I

[*] Some time later, I met a Lebanese girl, and without telling her anything of the story, I asked her what *kulu enta* meant. "*Kulu enta?*" she said, musingly. "*Kulu enta* would mean: You eat it."

was all too ready to believe myself the one to whom all things come. I savored his theory as I had savored his dinner. But unfortunately, there is a problem. Uncle Manuel was right that if Old Elias got his name aboard that ship, the Egyptians might have named him as easily as the Greeks. Implicit in his theory is that any name must tell something not only about the person named but of the person naming. For example, the name Kakoyanis (Bad John) does not necessarily mean that its original bearer was an evil person. It means that some other person had a reason to call him evil. With the place names, the relationship between named and namer is most evident. To be called Halkitis, a man must first go away from Halki. For the same reason, although it is possible that the Egyptians gave Old Elias a nickname, it is very unlikely they would call him Kulu Enta, stressing his ability to snatch the coins from them. That would be the last thing about him they would wish to immortalize, and whatever the nickname might have been, it would rather emphasize a weakness than strength. However seductive the similarity of *kulu enta* may be, it is an accident.

For the next theory, we turn to Uncle George. We were sitting in an automat on 59th Street, not far from where I'd had the previous discussion with Uncle Manuel. Uncle George liked to eat there, because he could have a Kasiot delicacy which he could have nowhere else in town. Horn and Hardart's did not actually prepare the delicacy themselves; in fact, they have certainly never heard of it. Nevertheless, Uncle George was able to create it by combining a plate of rice and a plate of baked beans. Mixing them together until they had an even consistency, he would approximate the Kasiot *fako-rizo*, a paste of beans and rice.

"In the Kasiot dialect," said Uncle George, eating his *fako-rizo*, "there is a certain word you may find interesting, *kuluki*, which means little dog. That is what they used to call us, in our childhood in Kasos. '*Kuluki*,' they used to say, to me and Basil and Manuel, too, 'Come here, you *Kuluki*.'

"Once, I was talking to an old captain of a generation earlier than my father. He had known Old Elias himself, and he told me that when the harbormaster asked his other name, Old Elias hesitated and then, blushingly he said, 'If you like, they call me Kulukas.'"

"Kulukas?"

"That's what this captain said."

"And what does that mean?"

"Big dog. Big *kuluki*." That was his nickname at the time. According to the captain, Old Elias was not a very goodlooking man. He may have been tall and agile, but his features were rather crude: he had a bulbous nose that may have suggested a snout, and his whole countenance may have been dog-like."

"I prefer Uncle Manuel's theory."

"Of course. But is it true? If Kulukundis comes from *kulu enta* as he said, what about the second K, the one that must be inserted somehow between kulu and enta. Where did it come from? If Kulukundis comes from *kulukas,* then the second K is already there: the first five letters are the same."

"But what about the last letters?" I said, in my accustomed role. "How do you get Kulukundis from Kulukas?"

"Kulukas would be a crude nickname, said Uncle George, "and the harbormaster may have wanted to soften it by adding the more genteel ending *tis*. By the way, no wonder Old Elias blushed. If he said his name was Kulukas, the cause is clear. But what was the shame in Kulu Enta? In any case, Kulukatis would be difficult to say, so the harbormaster may have put in another U and N to make Kulukuntis,° and that became Old Elias' name from that day forth."

I returned to Uncle Manuel, to tell him my bad news.

° The actual Greek spelling of the name. We transliterated it into English as Kulukundis, to avoid arousing people two ways instead of one.

"So you are bothered by a little K?" he said. "You scholars are too demanding with your evidence. If the facts don't give you a theory by themselves, you must help them a little, with your imagination. Even your Uncle George gives his theory a little push. He says the harbormaster might have added a U and N to come up with Kulukundis. But as long as you are adding letters, why not add my little K. Why add two letters to derive yourself from a little dog, and not a single K to be the man to whom all things come, as you call him. If you insist on the Kuluki, there is room in my theory for him too. The Greek sailors on the ships were mostly Kasiots, captured in 1824, and they all knew that dialect word for dog. So that's where your *kuluki* may come in, to supply the final K. They heard *kulu enta*, and they thought of *kuluki* and combined all the sounds together to make Kulukundis. As for the blushing, who told you he blushed for shame? It might have been for modesty. Wouldn't you blush to tell someone you are the man to whom all things come?"

Just before our trip to Kasos, we were spending a few days in Iraklion in Crete waiting for the boat. I was wandering around in a museum of medieval Greek history, and I found a photograph of a ridge of mountains taken from a distance across a high plateau. Beneath the photograph was the caption: "A view from Anoyia, looking toward the Kulukuna Range."

I found Uncle George and led him to the photograph. He stood silently for several minutes.

"What are you suggesting?" he said.

For an answer, I put my finger over the final A, leaving the remainder, Kulukun.

"You may be right," said Uncle George.

The possibility was even more compelling when I remembered the rules about the formation of names from places. Halkitis is the man from Halki, Roditis from Rhodes. In every case, a *tis* is added to make the person who comes from that place. So what can you do with Kulukuna, to indicate the one from that region. Kulukunatis sounds awkward to the native ear. It would be much simpler to drop the A and add the *tis* directly to the stem, arriving at Kulukuntis, (Kulukundis, begging your pardon).

At last we found it. All things come to him who waits, and every dog will have his day. My uncles had been searching for a nickname, simply because they could not find the name in any of the other categories. They had not suspected that the name, though Greek, might not be a nickname but a place name after all.

Old Elias or some ancestor of his must have been a Cretan, a native of that region in the Kulukuna Mountains. Seeking wider horizons, he must have left his birthplace and settled in another part of Greece. There, remembering the valley of his childhood, he spoke of it so often that the people of his adopted country thought of him as the one who came from the Kulukunas. In that I-thou polarity which is inherent in a name and identifies not only the person named but the person naming, they called him the one who came from the Kulukuna: Kulukundis.

Some years later, either that man or one of his descendants sought new horizons and traveled eastward to the island of Kasos. The history of Crete has been so turbulent that it has continually pumped out its population to other islands—the Ionian, the Cyclades, and the Dodecanese. It may have been at the time of one of the Cretan uprisings against the Venetians or the Turks. Or it may have been during the Revolution of 1821 when twenty-five hundred Cretans took refuge in Kasos. Old Elias himself might have been the one. He might have been one of the five hundred armed Cretans crouching beside the Kasiots at the rampart. Then, in the debacle that followed, he was taken prisoner by Ismael and put to work as a slave sailor on an Egyptian man-of-war. And the rest of the story is remembered history.

"But if Kulukundis comes from Kulukuna," said Uncle George, "it must have been Old Elias' surname by the time he went to Syros. And if so, why did he tell the harbormaster first that he was simply Elias of George?"

A good question. It was the key to why my uncles misunderstood the name, looking for its origin as a nickname.

"I'll tell you why," I told my uncle, taking on a new role at last.

I knew Old Elias had not volunteered his surname because he was not accustomed to using it, but he *had* it just the same. Even though a Kasiot had a surname, it was not unusual for him to be known just by his first name and patronymic. I was soon to see the proof of this in Kasos. When Aphrodite asked who I was, my uncle could hardly tell her I was Elias Kulukundis. That would have told her nothing, and it would not even have distinguished me from the other Elias Kulukundis standing at my side. Instead, he told her I was Elias of Michael, identifying me by my father, exactly as Old Elias identified himself to the harbormaster.

And that solves the final riddle: the blushing. The blush had nothing to do with modesty for being the man to whom all things come nor shame for being the *kuluki*. It was embarrassment for having given the wrong answer. To identify yourself to a stranger in a foreign place as though he were a native of your village is reason for embarrassment. That I know from personal experience. Over a century later, I told the kindergarten teacher I was Elias, answering her as though she were a familiar figure in my world, a world where up to then I had needed no last name. Then, at the age of five, I learned a lesson my ancestor had learned at twenty-five. If I blushed to say at last that my other name was Kulukundis, the teacher must have guessed the reason without knowing either a legend arisen among Egyptian sailors or the Kasiot word for dog.

In the time remaining before the boat, we set out for the Kulukunas. We expected no actual confirmation of my theory;

we only wanted to see that range of mountains I believed must be our ultimate place of origin. But at the same time, we could not resist performing some experiments. Stopping in villages along the road, we would ask questions. First, how would the villagers call someone from the Kulukunas? Then, if that failed, did they know of anyone named Kulukundis?

But we were almost at the Kulukunas themselves before anyone had even heard of them. At the mention of the name, the villagers looked at us curiously. Even here, near the place of origin, the name was still strange and amusing, its syllables still bizarre and foreign to the ear. With the same smirk and shrug we had come to expect during our long exile on foreign shores, these villagers shook their heads dumbly to all our questions.

Finally, we identified the Kulukunas as a hump of land standing directly beside the sea, across a valley that opened downward from the northern slopes of Mt. Ida. That was another disappointment. The Kulukunas are discouragingly small. They are not even mountains, but hills: brief interruptions in the level of the land. There are only three of them, and only one is the Kulukuna, lending its title to the other nameless two. They are absolutely bare, simply pointed rocks. They hardly have time to rise to their pitiful height before they slope downward again, to the sea. South of them is a fertile valley, with olive, almond, and lemon trees in differing shades of green. Nearby, there are villages: Perama, the largest one, on the main highway from Iraklion to Rethymnon; another named Melidhoni, between Perama and the sea; and a third, at the foot of the Kulukuna itself.

We went to Melidhoni first and began to ask our questions. As soon as we sat down in the café on the square, the entire male population of the village had gathered around us.

For a start, I said: "By the way, how do you people call yourselves?"

Thirty faces looked at me.

"I mean, how do you refer to yourselves when you speak to people from other places?"

More silence and blank looks.

"I mean, what do you *call* yourselves. Not just Cretans. You must have some other name."

"Melidhonites!" someone said at last, and instantly a murmur of relief passed around the assembly.

"Yes, yes," they were declaring now. "Melidhonites. We call ourselves Melidhonites."

"Just Melidhonites?" I said. "Don't you have some other name?"

But having discovered their name they were not to be deprived of it.

"Don't you think of yourselves as people from this entire region?" I said. "Aren't you also people from the Kulukunas?"

"No," said the spokesman. "All people from Melidhoni are Melidhonites and all people from the Perama are Peramites."

"That may be true," I said. "But I think all you Melidhonites and Peramites are also people from the Kulukunas and therefore you could all be Kulukundis'!"

At least, Uncle Manuel cannot say I am unwilling to give a theory a little push: as long as it is *my* theory. I'll push it like a coolie. But these unregenerate Melidhonites refused any sort of *Enosis* with their neighbors the Peramites. Besides, they looked at me as those I were insane.

"No, we have no such names here," someone said, in conciliation.

Instantly I turned on him. "What do you mean no such names? What names?"

"No names like that," he said. "Like Kuluku . . . or whatever you said. There is no single name for the entire region. We are Melidhonites or Peramites depending on what village we come from."

So he granted that Kulukundis could be a place name after all. He recognized it as a name that might be given to someone from Kulukuna, if that had been the practice, despite the fact, as he assured me, that it wasn't the practice. That was some progress anyway. Once you granted that Kulukundis might be the name given a person from this place, the next question would be how that person would be called if he journeyed to another part of Crete, where the distinction between Peramite and Melidhonite would be less significant.

Then, in Perama, we asked the café-keeper so many questions he decided to send for the schoolteacher, the town scholar. This man had been to study in Athens, and could tell us everything. He sent a nephew to bring the teacher, and we waited for the poor man to be routed from his nap. Soon he appeared, blinking in the sudden sunlight. We offered him a coffee, and he told us what he knew.

It was not much. As to the name of someone who came from the region of the Kulukunas, he could not risk a guess. As a last resort, I posed the final question: did he know anyone named Kulukundis?

His eyes brightened.

"Yes, I do," he said.

"You do?" I said. "Really?"

"Yes, yes," he said, enthusiastic now that he was finally able to help.

"Where does he live?" I said. I was enthusiastic too.

"There is not just one, there are many of them," he said.

"Well, where do they live?"

"They don't live here anymore. They have gone away."

"Gone away from the Kulukunas?"

"What *Kulukunas?* Gone away from Greece. They are a shipping family of five brothers, and they have all gone away to England and America."

So, like *kulu enta* and the *kuluki,* my theory must remain a speculation. As to my uncles' theories, I do not discard them. Though I do not believe they are the origin of Kulukundis, they might as well have been. Though neither of them is true, they both are.

Uncle Manuel believed his name meant the man to whom all things come, interpreting it in the way he saw himself. In his ancestor, he saw a brave sailor who swam ashore as a derelict in 1826 and by the Crimean War had become the owner of four ships. To be sure, by the end of his life, Old Elias had lost his ships: his sons, George Elias and the others, saw to that. But it does not matter. The fortunes of a seafarer go up and down with the sea. And whatever his fortunes may be at any time, to a man to whom all things come, hope is an eternal spring.

Uncle George, on the other hand, seems hardly the man to whom all things come. He is bashful and retiring. He would rather eat at the automat than in the finest dining room in town, and of all his many assets, what he holds most precious are his capacity for invention and his sense of humor. Though these are not necessarily the attributes of a stalwart swimmer and founder of a breed of champions, they are very necessary to a man who suspects he can claim no nobler lineage than a dog's and must carry on in spite of it.

But even if I could confirm my theory with conclusive proof, it would bring us no closer to the mystery of Kulukundis. For the riddle of a family, I have substituted the riddle of a mountain, and the bizarre repetition of syllables—*ku-lu-ku*—is still as much of a mystery as ever. The natives of the region were no help in solving it. They were even a little embarrassed to hear us say the name, not imagining how familiar to us it really was. Apparently, even in its original usage, it must have been a cause of blushing.

Someday, we must solve that mystery. Perhaps in the generation after me, there will be someone compelled to explore the past. Perhaps a nephew of my own will be able to pick up the trail of that ancient Kulukundis and tramp into the wilds of Crete to discover a civilization antedating even Kasos. Or perhaps, instead of one nephew there will be two, disputing with each other. Perhaps they will look into all the chapters of Cretan history—Turkish, Venetian, Arabic, Roman, Hellenic, Dorian, Minoan, Phoenician—and trace out our lineage in contradictory directions. Perhaps one will find we are Arabs, dating our lineage from that dark emigration which passed across the Mediterranean like a cloud before the sun. And perhaps the other will contend that we came from an opposite direction, with a sunny party of Venetians sailing eastward at a later date.

But Hellenic pride makes me hope that neither of these answers will be true. I like to think that there have been Kulukundis' in the Aegean as long as there have been Greeks. I hope these two explorers of the future will look back beyond all the intervening waves that have ever crossed the Archipelago and discover that we antedate them all. Then, at some time in the future, these two explorers may take up the mystery of *kuluku* and dispute whether it is a name given by Phoenician sailors to a breed of champions, or some indecipherable Minoan for household pet. Then perhaps there will be still another explorer, some nephew of these nephews, who will assemble all their evidence and reflect on it and decide that neither theory is true. Perhaps this nephew, audacious enough to refute his uncles, will decide that the word Kuluku comes from still further back, from yet another island.

And so, from nephew to nephew the task will be handed on, and as each nephew makes his appearance in the future, he will be responsible for a region of the past, until finally by the time the string of nephews has extended to eternity, the chain of inquiry will extend back as far as it can go, and all the millennia of history will be charted. Then when the arc of time has leapt out to the ultimates and both extremes have been embraced, both the fire of creation and the crack of doomsday will appear as one flash, illuminating the same sky. Then, in that apocalyptic light, the world will appear in the outline both of its origin and its end, and that form will no doubt appear in the outline of an island. In the red lettering of revelation, the name of that island will be inscribed upon the sky, and in the language of the eternal, the message will be nothing less than the secret of the universe, though to us untutored mortals who cannot decipher it, the syllables will take the form of the ancient riddle we have been spelling to each other at every turn, another fragment with no beginning and no end, which is more a stutter than a song, a sound which in the ear of God must be the source of serene contentment, but to us mortals is the cause of shrugs and smiles and all our blushing: *kuluku, kuluku, kuluku-lukuluku.*

The Way
to Phry

*A*s we awoke on our first morning in Kasos, my Uncle must have been thinking of his brother Basil. Basil is the lost brother, the only one I have never called Uncle, the only one my father never knew because Basil died in 1907 and my father was born in 1906.

"Basil used to be very nimble and quick," Uncle George told us, sipping the tea Aphrodite had brought with our breakfast. "We used to take voyages on my father's ship, the *Anastasia*. The first mate was my father's cousin, Mavrandonis; we took his cabin so that he had to sleep in the chartroom. Once Mavrandonis was about to put on a new bowler hat, but Basil ran in suddenly, took the hat, and floated it in a trough of soapy water where Aphrodite used to wash the clothes.

"Afterword, Basil became very quiet. Perhaps that was the beginning of his illness. He began to shake, his sight gradually diminished, and his head declined to the right. Then, father came home to Syros with the *Anastasia*. Apparently, he must have been in the Black Sea where there was cholera, because he was in quarantine and couldn't come ashore. Mother went to the Port Office to confer with him. Should she take Basil to Athens for an operation? Apparently, by that time, they knew it was a tumor of the brain. But what could father say? What did he know? He said, 'Do whatever God reveals to you.' "

"My mother decided to have the operation, and she took Basil to Athens. We did not go with him, first because of the expenses of such a journey, and then because we had school. Basil was in good spirits as he left. He wore a peaked cap which Father had brought. Actually, Father had meant it for me, but I didn't like it, and so to please Father, Basil wore it himself. And he wore it that day, on the long journey."

Uncle George said no more. After breakfast, we put on bathing suits under our clothes and prepared to walk the two miles from our house to Ammoua, the only sandy beach on Kasos. We set out along a footpath, high above the sea, leading westward from the town of Phry along the northern shore of the island.

The last Phrydiot houses thinned away, and below we could see a pool of salt water, called "the lake," a few yards from the sea, fed by waves breaking on the iron coast. We walked on, leaving the town behind us, past plots of earth enclosed in their walls of stone: grim fortresses against the indomitable goat, a vine or two growing in their citadel. We walked past a derelict mill high above the sea: a stone turret, crippled and blind, its blades looted and sold for firewood.

Uncle George thought of Yeroyiannis and his *tsifliki,* or large estate, which he remembered in his childhood had been somewhere along this path. He walked ahead, his trousers belted high, a bathtowel wrapped around his head for shelter from the sun. Suddenly he stopped and looked back at me: black sun-glasses wrapped in a shroud of white cloth. He said:

> "And so old Yeroyiannis son,
> Made himself two *tsiflikia*.
> The one is full of *lapatha*
> The other full of *fikia*."

Lapatha is a weed that grows inland; *fikia* grow near the sea.
Like all estates in Kasos, whether inland or near the sea,
Yeroyiannis' *tsifliki* was a kingdom of weeds.

We walked on past the small chapel of St. George of the
Spring, in the craggy ravine of a rain torrent. The eulogy to
Yeroyiannis' kingdom made slow repetitions as we walked. At
Ammoua we had a swim, near Antiperatos. At the top of the
hill above, we could see the houses of Ayia Marina, silent
and white as tombstones.

After our swim, we turned back on the way to Phry. The
weather had cleared and Karpathos bloomed out of its mem-
brane of white mist, so close that Kasos and Karpathos seemed
one island, the sea like quicksilver poured into all its coves
and turnings. Suddenly we saw a steamer turning silently in the
empty sea: the *Arcadia,* the ship which brought us the day
before, stopping in Kasos once again on its return journey
from Rhodes to Crete. It seemed an apparition, materializing
suddenly. And it made my uncle think of the day in 1898 when
he and his younger brother Basil were walking on that very
path, when the *Dhekeli,* the Turkish steamer from Alexandria,
appeared suddenly on that empty disc, with its *hapari.*

Uncle George was six years old, and Basil was four. The
year before, there had been a disastrous war with Turkey,
the year Aphrodite remembered when the Cretan revolution
reddened the horizon with fire and blood. When war broke
out, the Dardanelles were closed to all Greek ships, and the
Anastasia, bound for Russia with an unprofitable cargo of roof-
tiles, had to lay up in Syros for the duration of the war. The
family spent the winter with her: Captain Elias and Eleni,

George and Basil, baby Nicholas, and Manuel in his mother's womb.

In the spring, when the war was over and the knot of Greek ships was loosened once again in the Syros harbor, Captain Elias set out at last for the Black Sea to deliver the wretched roof-tiles. There he picked up a cargo of grain for Alexandria, and on that journey, Eleni would accompany him because her brother who was a doctor in Alexandria had just become engaged, and she wanted to be present with her husband at the *emvasmata*, the feast celebrating the engagement. That way, too, Eleni could see her sister Virginia who had moved from Kasos to Alexandria, and was doomed to die there during her elder sister's visit.

On the way, they stopped at Kasos, to leave the older boys. George and Basil would stay in Kasos, in the care of Aphrodite and their grandmother, Marigo.

They stayed in Kasos just long enough to take the two boys ashore, the *Anastasia* anchoring in the lee of Makra Island because the north wind was blowing and the ship could not anchor near the unprotected Kasiot coast. The caique must have gone out to meet her, across the windy passage, plying the waves as stubbornly as a donkey. And the whole town of Phry must have been watching as the caique returned with Eleni and the two boys, their shaven heads poking up from the stern like toy balls: two frightened, diminutive cavaliers riding the white horses home to Phry.

They were left to the tender mercies of their grandmother, Eleni's mother, who lived to have great-grandchildren yet hated children, who was so blinded by grief and rage on hearing the *hapari* of her daughter Virginia's death that according to Aphrodite, she swooped down on George and Basil and made for the well with them.

Marigo was illiterate, and the letters of her name on the needlework tapestry must have been drawn for her by someone else, and she must have stitched them with no more comprehension than she would have had of the curls and spirals of Arabic. But her husband Vasilios Mavroleon was highly educated. He was a merchant, a shareholder in sailing ships though he himself was not a captain; and eventually he was elected *demogeront* from the town of Phry. Vasilios thoroughly documented the transactions of his life, and there is no telling what resources he might have left us family historians. But his archives met calamity. Old Yia-Yia had an abhorrence of old papers which my uncle swears (and I affirm) has been passed down to all the females of the family, including—mysteriously—those who have married into it. There is a Kasiot saying that "the bride, from the time of her birth, grows up to resemble her mother-in-law." And if this mysterious theory is true, then all the females of the family, all the present paper-destroyers and obscurantists, are descended originally from Old Yia-Yia.

After her husband's death, year by year, for the remainder of her life in the house with the blue shutters, she tore out pages of the old man's ledgers, fastened them in a little loose-leaf binder and hung them on a nail in the outhouse across the courtyard. My uncle, visiting that chamber in 1910, found installments of the old man's records doomed to a service Vasilios had not foreseen.

To this gentle humanist, the boys were consigned. She would put them to bed while the sun was still high in the sky, lock the door of the bedroom, and go visiting. On these nights, George was frightened. It was cold in the bed alone with Basil, for they were used to their mother sleeping with them. And at that time —before the advent of electricity—the streets were full of horrible imaginings: *striglas* and nereids, and women who had died in childbirth and were thought to rise. Sometimes a dog, glutted and crazed with eating lambs would howl weirdly. And once, the mad girl of Phry who went around wearing a coarse blanket and her father's underclothes, came up the stairway from the street, calling their mother who was not there but in Alexandria, calling gently, "Kyra Eleni! Kyra Eleni!"

In the meantime, their parents had departed for Alexandria, to be present at the *emvasmata* of Eleni's brother, the Uncle-Doctor, as the boys called him. My uncle remembers him distinctly from a picture he saw only once: the Uncle-Doctor with his handle-bar moustache sitting with his fiancée in the first row of a family portrait, taken by a professional photographer of Alexandria, not at an engagement, or at a wedding, but unexpectedly around Virginia's open coffin.

But at the time the boys knew nothing of it, since such *haparia* were not for children's ears. Years later, my uncle pieced it together in Syros. He brought a friend home from school and they were making an experiment with sulphuric acid, and in his mother's hearing, he pronounced the word *aqua-fortis*. When his mother heard it, she drew her breath in sharply, making a hissing sound which meant that George had just said something very bad. Then, under her breath she muttered "God forgive her." And so George knew—he knew by that evidence—that what Aphrodite had told him was true, that Virginia, his mother's sister, had been poisoned in Alexandria with *aqua-fortis*.

My uncle remembers seeing Aunt Virginia only once. He was sitting on the courtyard wall of the house in Kasos, and Aunt Virginia was coming across the courtyard, dressed in a pink robe, with her hair beautifully done. And the mischievous, shaven imp —my uncle—greeted her with an obscene remark which she ignored, and stroked his hair. That is all he remembers, except her umbrella with the thick handle of sculptured roses and the ivory fan, which Eleni kept with her all her life, and the photograph taken by an open coffin.

One day, two weeks or so after Eleni and Captain Elias had left, another aunt, Captain Elias' sister, took the boys to spend the day at her house in another part of Phry. Basil was so unhappy in the new surroundings he cried all the time and would not eat. He wanted Aphrodite, and so the aunt let them go home again after lunch, and George took him by the hand and led him back through the devious streets of Phry. They had no trouble finding the house, because of the pine tree which was growing in the courtyard. There was only one other like it in all of Kasos, and the two of them stood high above the town of Phry like two masts above a ship.

When they arrived, they found the door was locked and no one answered even though George too, joining Basil, was calling, "Aphrodite, Aphrodite!" The family was at Vasilios' summer house on the outskirts of Ayia Marina, with a terrace overlooking the sea all the way from Armathia to the foot of Karpathos. Grandmother had gone there for the afternoon with Aphrodite, thinking the children were safe at their aunt's. At that hour of the afternoon, all the neighbors were asleep, as the two children stood beneath the shuttered windows calling into the silent house, "Aphrodite, Aphrodite!"

George guessed where they must be, and he thought he knew the way. He picked his way along the stoney path, Basil following, ominously silent now when he should have been more anxious than ever for his Aphrodite. But George forgot to turn back down toward the Bucca before turning up to Ayia Marina. Instead he went down toward the sea, past the Chapel of St. Nicholas, past the last Phrydiot houses where the path winds out above the sea and you can see "the lake" glistening below like a turquoise in a casing of stone. Then, after the last Phrydiot houses thinned away, they came to a solitary mill, blades hovering like a becalmed sailing ship, and George remembered the *mandinadha* Aphrodite had taught him about this mill which belonged to a man named Yeroyiannis:

> "And so old Yeroyiannis son
> Made himself two *tsiflikia*.
> The one is full of *lapatha*,
> The other full of *fikia*."

And now George knew there must be something wrong, for this couldn't be the way to the summer house. It was the way to "the lake" for swimming, the way to St. George of the Spring, to Ammoua. It was too late to change course now. The path wound downhill toward the shore, and the way to the summer house was inland. George looked up and saw the town of Ayia,Marina, crowning the top of the hill, but to get there they would have to climb through many fields, over many crisscrossing dry-stone walls, into the blinding white wall of the sun itself.

So they turned back on the way to Phry. Basil followed quietly, watching the steps and ledges in the stone where he put his feet. The air had cleared and Karpathos had bloomed suddenly out of the mist. Now it looked so close that Kasos and Karpathos seemed one island, the sea surrounding it like quicksilver. Then suddenly, they saw the ship turning silently: the *Dhekeli,* the Turkish steamer that passed by Kasos weekly on its way through the Archipelago from Alexandria to Smyrna.

"Look George," Basil cried, "there's a *digla.*" He meant *strigla,* but he was only four. And George too, found something magical about this ship. Its painted funnels seemed red hot, as though glowing with the fire of its engines. At the sight of it, they forgot the summer house. They quickened their steps, picking their way over the precarious terrain, racing to reach the Bucca in time to be there standing on tip-toe among the crowd on the breakwater. But they had only reached Yeroyiannis' windmill when the whistle sounded. By the time they reached the town, the last caiques had already been stuffed into the Bucca and Kasos was already gobbling all the news, relishing this weekly ingestion from the world beyond. There was the usual kissing and weeping, showers of black robes and cowls, litanies of welcome.

As George and Basil played among the luggage all set out in the square in front of the Church of St. Spiridon, the sky was deepening. The smell of frying fish in the unshuttered square windows made them know it was time to eat. And so they made for home, through the devious Phrydiot streets, making for the pine tree that rose above the town like a mast. As usual, there were dogs barking, the whine of a lyre, the staccato of a grandmother calling a child; and in addition, among all the other sounds, there was a slow, insistent wailing.

It became louder as they picked their way toward the pine tree. There was no one wailing in any house they passed. Instead there were silent faces at the windows: women and children watching. Now the wailing was louder still. As they started down the last row of Phrydiot houses lined up before the sea, they saw all the neighbors on their balconies. They were near the house now. George saw the front gate was open and swinging, and also the door to the kitchen, and the door on the balcony above and all the shutters. George quickened his steps now, leading Basil by the hand, for now he knew the wailing was coming from his house. The last time George had seen all the doors and shutters open was at the christening of his brother Nicholas or his father's name-day. But this was not a christening and not a feast. The doors and windows of that house hung loosely open now like a new widow who has cut the tight knot at the back of her head and for the first time let her hair hang down in mourning.

Aphrodite was at the gate. George had thought they could slip in unnoticed, up the stairs to the bedroom above. But Aphrodite saw them before they could escape, and so George put his head down like a donkey about to be beaten, Basil following. They stumbled through the doorway, their eyes shut and faces already wincing. But strangely, when George opened his eyes again, they were past her, inside the courtyard. Aphrodite did not seem to notice them. Around the corner, on the upper veranda, George could hear the wails.

"Charon, what did I do to you," he heard a woman cry, "that you took my little bird from me?"

"And clothed my body," cried another, "in eternal black."

Then, behind them, he heard Aphrodite say, very politely, "Please come in." They are all upstairs on the veranda."

And now, George knew there were more visitors about to appear behind them, and he knew there was no turning back now. Timidly, he led Basil toward the veranda. He hesitated at the corner of the house, because he always felt a moment of uncertainty when there were guests on the veranda, even on a normal day. He was always afraid the women would shriek and cackle at him and kiss him. And for a moment, that was what he thought would happen, as he and Basil went around and the voices rose up suddenly. For a moment he thought it was for him: that sudden explosion of women's screams.

But it wasn't. No one looked at the two boys, as they took their places in that strange assembly.

The women were sitting on cushions in a wide semi-circle on the veranda floor. They were all in black, their cowls thrown back, their hair loose and hanging down over their foreheads in two separate strands. The women were rocking and twisting as though there were something terrible hurting them. They screamed and wailed and pulled ferociously on their locks of hair. Some of them were tearing at their dresses. Their black sleeves were shredded and they drew their nails mercilessly through the cloth and into their uncovered flesh. Then, suddenly, one woman sitting closest to George and Basil stopped her wailing and turned to them with an eye as clear and cold as glass and said, "Sit down, children. What are you standing up for?"

So George sat down all at once, pulling Basil down with him on the same cushion. Now he looked more closely at the faces beneath those angry lashing curls, and he realized that every woman on the veranda was someone he knew. They were all the women of the neighborhood, women he had seen every day of his life. With their hair undone, they seemed strangers to him. And now at last, George felt his own inhaling breath make the sharp hissing sound as he realized that the woman sitting in the very center of that semi-circle was his grandmother. It was Old Yia-Yia. Her cowl was thrown back and her hair hung over her face in two strands. Her black dress was torn and she was digging her nails into her flesh. George felt his breath taken suddenly away. He had no breath to speak to her. At the sight of her, with her hair lashing about her face like the serpents of the Medusa, he felt himself turned to stone.

Now a single woman's voice rose up above the rest. It was the midwife and exorcist, who was also a *lamentatrice* for the dead, who sang the dirge of Christ every Good Friday, as the bier of Christ was carried through the smoky streets of Phry.

"Oh, miserable mother," she cried, "you should have kissed your daughter's wedding crown." The singer was sitting in the center of the group, her face lifted to the sky, her voice was shrill as a violin. Around her all the women sobbed in unison, pulling at their separated braids of hair, giving short stabbing cries of pain.

"Oh, miserable mother, you should have kissed your daughter's crown."

"Goo! Goo! Goo!" the women moaned, still in unison, faster, pulling harder at their hair.

"Oh, miserable mother, you should have kissed your daughter's crown," she cried again, for the last time, the chorus responding, pulling harder, crying in rhythmic pain.

"And instead you kissed her forehead in the coffin."

Now the screams were not in unison. Each woman cried randomly as she tore at her hair and clothes and flesh. The bodies writhed and shuddered. Some of the women had torn their dresses open in front, uncovering their breasts, pulling and pinching.

Now the women called different names. They were not wailing only for the miserable mother, but each one was wailing for herself, lamenting a kinsman she herself had kissed in death.

"Oh, my Yani, the bitter sea was your Communion!"

"Oh, my Nicola, black blood is flowing from my heart for you!"

Then the waves of passion quieted. The women's heads fell forward on their breasts, their hands hung harmless at their sides. Their eyes were closed; their bodies swayed gently, throbbing into stillness. The entire circle was silent, heads bowed, like sleeping birds.

Uncle George does not remember it, but according to Aphrodite, when grandmother saw him and Basil, she got all excited and came after them as though to throw them down the cistern. Of course, it was just for show, but her idea was to take revenge on their mother who had let Virginia die in Alexandria. Anyway, Aphrodite said, just to be sure, she locked them up in bedroom until the wailing marathon was over.

And that was the last they ever heard of Aunt Virginia. Her story was buried with her body, to flower darkly once in Aphrodite's clandestine narration and once again, years later, in a sigh emanating from Eleni's soul. The only relics of her life are the ivory fan and the umbrella with its sculptured roses on its handle which Eleni kept with her always beside the icons of the house, and the photograph: an assembly of mourners gathered at an open bier.

I was shocked to see it, no less than I would have been to see the corpse itself, peeping up at us under the rising lid of an old wedding chest. It was the first such photograph I had ever seen, though they were as common as their opposites, the pictures of infants lately born.

That afternoon, after we returned from Ammoua, my cousin had seen an end of Aunt Virginia sticking out among dusty glassware and broken crockery in that place euphemistically called a living room. He got hold of her and pulled and kept pulling until she came out. And then the whole house was chaos: my uncle at the table, one astonished nephew over either shoulder, and Aunt Virginia supine on his knees. Around us, Aphrodite swooped and fluttered, stopping a moment to look herself, then continuing her gyrations.

In the picture was an open coffin enclosing a young slender figure. The casket was tilted slightly, and the young woman's head was turned toward the camera. Her cheeks were round and youthful, the eyelids gently closed, her lips faintly touching in a suggestion of a smile. Around the forehead was a crown of lemon blossoms worn by a bride. Behind her, the length of the coffin, stood relatives in mourning, men in the stiff high collars of the time, women in black robes, bareheaded, their hair let down and parted in the middle in two separating locks.

"It's Virginia," my uncle said. "You see the crown?"

He explained for our sake. A married woman might be buried with her wedding crown around her forehead. But an unmarried woman might also wear a crown to emphasize the poignancy of her untimely death, since of all bridegrooms, Charon was the one to win her.

"This is the picture I saw many years ago," my uncle said. "The one taken in Alexandria in 1898 which my mother kept all her life along with the ivory fan and the umbrella with the sculptured roses. And there, in the first row of mourners, you see my mother."

We looked again, and sitting directly behind the coffin, we saw Eleni. It was the first and only picture I have seen of her. She was dressed in black, bareheaded, her dark hair loosened and falling on either side of her face, not in angry lashing snakes, but in perfectly combed and orderly cascades of grief. In her face there was no mark of violence or distorting passion. She was perfectly composed, glowing with the serenity of a woman complete either in joy or grief. She seemed unaware of anyone else, her eyes resting on the cradled face before her in distant rapture.

But was my uncle right? Was it Virginia? If that were the photograph taken in Alexandria in 1898, where was Uncle-Doctor and his fiancée? And where was Captain Elias, who should have been sitting beside his wife, keeping the vigil with her? Perhaps these uncertainties began to trouble my uncle even then, though he said nothing to us, only gazed musingly at the photograph before him, as one by one we left him to keep a lonely vigil by the corpse.

By evening we had the answer. My cousin and I were sitting on the terrace between the houses. There was silence all around us, except for the comforting background of an island's evening sounds. Before us, Karpathos was fading in the darkness.

Then, suddenly, we heard noises that would not have been out of place on that terrace sixty years before. We hurried into Uncle George's room, wondering what new *hapari* had arrived. There were no words, only noises, uttered with precision as though they were phonemes of an intelligible language.

Uncle George was in his undershirt and slippers. Behind him, Aphrodite loomed. On his knees, he held another photograph, another corpse. A second one had surfaced on a new tide of old letters and broken crockery.

"Don't you have eyes to see, George?" Aphrodite said. "I tell you it's a boy."

"How can it be a boy?" my uncle said, making a snap in his voice that should have meant the end of any argument.

"I'll tell you how," said Aphrodite. "Because it *is* a boy. Do you understand Romaic? Or shall I explain it to you in Arabic? It is a boy."

"How can it be a boy?" my uncle said. "Don't you see the wedding crown? You don't bury a boy with a crown around his head. I tell you it's Virginia. It is not a boy."

We were crowding behind my uncle now. There was another casket, with no relatives behind it. The photo was larger, the coffin yielding a closer view. Boy or girl, it was a young person: cheeks round and youthful, lips gently touching in another hint of smile, around the forehead another crown of lemon.

"I don't know who it is," I said. "But there is one thing I *do* know."

To my surprise, they stopped shouting and looked at me.

"Whoever it is," I said, "it's the same person who's in the other picture, the one with the people all around it and Eleni sitting in the first row."

"And that's Virginia," my uncle said.

My cousin ran to bring the other picture. In a few moments, I knew the mystery would be undone. All the questions would be answered: the absence of the Uncle-Doctor and his fiancée, the absence of Captain Elias. We awaited my cousin now like Oedipus' second messenger, the one who offers no new knowledge, only a message that will join two facts together, bringing them to bear, inevitably and tragically, on a single person. My uncle said nothing. He had taken his glasses off and was holding them like a magnifying glass against the sleeping face. Behind him, Aphrodite was quiet, waiting for the proof.

The proof arrived. They were the same person. The same cheeks, robust in death, the same faint smile, the same crown of lemon. As we held the photos side by side, they fit one into the other, like the pieces of a puzzle.

Now, details emerged from the first photo we hadn't seen before, as though it had come suddenly into focus. How could we have missed them before? Didn't we have eyes to see?

Aphrodite was triumphant. "Look at the cap beside him," she cried, "and the brass buttons on his jacket. It's a school uniform he's wearing. They buried him in his uniform from school and student's cap."

My uncle said nothing now. He said nothing because his mind was whirling rapidly through the years and miles, misconception giving way to truth. It was not Alexandria in 1898, it was Athens in 1907. That was why Uncle-Doctor and his bride-to-be and Captain Elias were not present. That was why Eleni, curiously, was sitting beside the bier in place reserved for the most bereaved of all, gazing at the face before her with the distant rapture of a Madonna Dolorosa. Now, my uncle knew, though Aphrodite could not have known, that it was not a student's cap the dead child had beside him. It was a peaked cap brought from Marseilles by Captain Elias for his first son George, the cap George had discarded and left for his younger brother, more dutiful than he, to take up and wear. He had been wrong: it was a boy. It was his brother Basil.

It was the first time he had seen that photo, or any evidence of Basil's death. Basil had embarked on the final voyage, standing at the rail of the steamship, waving George's own cap at him in farewell; and life in Syros had closed over his departure like the sea. George was studying, looking forward to the next day when he would take exams and school would be over for the summer, and when the *hapari* came, he was not waiting for it. The ship crept unseen around the promontory, with no sails of black to announce its deadly offering. George was coming home from school, wearing a blue flannel jacket with brass buttons, his books and papers under his arm. As he neared his house, he heard no wailing, saw no unshuttered windows and no flesh and clothing torn in grieving. Instead, he saw his brother John sitting on the wall. It was John who delivered the *hapari*, without emphasis, smiling perhaps in mischief, as though he were announcing a dirty word.

"George," he said, with perhaps some challenge in his voice, some indecorous pride to be the one to bear his older brother such a piece of news. "Basil's dead."

Now we were all still looking at the photograph. There was something uncanny about that sleeping face. The family resemblance was so great, it could have been Uncle George himself, in the uniform of the Syros high-school and his own peaked cap laid beside him. As a musing man of seventy-two, Uncle George could have been gazing at his own thirteen-year-old corpse, mirrored back at him in some bizarre reflection.

"But the wedding crown," said Aphrodite, reminding us of the one detail yet unexplained. "Why did they bury him with a crown around his head?"

It was not a challenge. Her voice was reverent. Unknowingly, she had only brought to light the final evidence, the slender physical marking—the scars remaining on the ankles of the king—which alone will seal the tragedy beyond a doubt.

"Because of the wound," my uncle said, without passion. "Basil died in an operation for a tumor of the brain. In the open coffin, his wounded head would have been unsightly, so they bound it with a crown of lemon. He fought bravely and was crowned."

The Unknown God

"In Kasos," said Uncle George, "a young girl prepared a mystic altar to an Unknown God. She worshipped him ahead of time, and when he came, she loved him and was devoted to him all her life."

The god was the young girl's future husband. The way a Kasiot marriage was arranged, the girl might be walking on the square in Phry, arm in arm with girl-friends. Meanwhile, in her courtyard, her father and her uncles might be talking to another father and other uncles. And by the end of that afternoon, by the time the young girl came home, the partner of her life would be chosen for her, and the day of her wedding would be set.

Until then, as my uncle said, she must keep an altar to an Unknown God. From her earliest childhood, she believed there was one man ordained to come for her. His coming had been foreknown on the seventh evening of her life, at the ceremony of "the seven," when as an infant in her cradle, she had lain in dreamless sleep while three women of antiquity were supposed to have hovered over her: the three Fates, one with a spindle and thread to spin out the infant's time on earth, the second with a scissors to cut it off at the appointed place, the third with an open ledger in which to write the infant's life. On that evening, while the rest of her family was sleeping, that shrouded trinity had ordained her future for her, including the identity of her mysterious Unknown God.

Throughout girlhood, she might pray to that ancient trinity, begging them for revelation. But the three stern women kept their secret, remaining deaf to the prayers of a maiden's heart.

Only once a year, each spring on the feast of *Kleithona*, if a girl were virtuous and faithfully performed a ritual, she might be granted a vision of her future husband.

The feast of *Kleithona* took place in June. The night before, a young boy would draw water from the cistern in the house of a newly married bride. In doing so, he could not speak, even if someone spoke to him.

"Don't say a word," hissed black-cowled maidens, with raised forefingers. "In the name of the Virgin, keep a cross upon your lips."

In sacred silence, the young boy would fill the barrel with water from the cistern and with the help of his black-cowled assistants, he would set the barrel on the roof. Now the water was "speechless water," possessed of magical powers. The black-cowled maidens would cover the barrel with a red handkerchief and seal it with a padlock to keep the potion pure. All night, the "speechless water" would sit on the housetop where the stars could see it and impregnate it with their powers of augury.

The next morning, on the feast of *Kleithona*, all the unmarried girls of the village would gather at this house of the newly married bride. Accompanied by mothers, aunts and cousins, they would make a circle in the courtyard, and the barrel of water would be brought down and set in the middle. Each unmarried girl would bring a ripened fruit, a pear or peach or pomegranate, stick a piece of jewelry in it so that it could be identified as hers, and lower it into the water.

Now a virtuous girl, one whose father and mother both were living, would be chosen to sit beside the barrel. Then, the *mandinadhas* would begin. One by one, each aged woman would recite a couplet of her family. Around the circle, a low poetic murmuring proceeded, delivered by the black-shrouded chorus, the venerable muses of the cowl:

> "Your body is a minaret,
> "Your shadow is a garden.
> "And all the moisture on your brow,
> "Is perfume from Arabia."

As soon as the *mandinadha* was over, the virtuous child would thrust down her virgin hand and draw out a pear or a peach or a pomegranate.

"My Kyrenia's!" cried a mother, recognizing a filigree earring or an Austrian coin in the fruit. All Kyrenia's friends would scream with pleasure, and Kyrenia would blush and keep her eyes on the pebbled courtyard floor. For she was the one whose body was a minaret, whose shadow was a garden, and the moisture of whose brow was perfume from Arabia.

One by one, the elder women sang their couplets, and one by one the fruits of the maidens were drawn from the "speechless water" by the virtuous girl presiding at the rim. Finally, each girl learned something either of herself or of her future husband, and blushed at the announcement, however inconclusive it might be.

Then, each girl would take home a glassful of the "speechless water," the potion fructified by the bejeweled fruits of every maiden in the village. And that night, before she went to bed, each girl would go out into her courtyard, with a red ribbon tied around her waist. She would take a mouthful from her glass of "speechless water" and two handfuls of barley. Then, in her nightgown, with the red ribbon around her waist, she would turn around in the center of the courtyard, lightly as a nereid. With her two hands full of barley and a sip of "speechless water" unswallowed in her mouth, she would turn faster and faster, her arms outstretched like the blades of a windmill. Then, turning as fast as she could go, she would open her fists so the barley would fly out and scatter against the courtyard walls. Then she would go to her room, drink down the rest of the "speechless water," and have a little wine and a salt *koulouri*° to disturb her sleep.

Then, with the red ribbon still around her waist, she would get into bed, and as she set her head against the pillow, she would murmur this prayer to the three black-shrouded women of antiquity:

> "In Hades my Fates are dancing,
>   And the Fate of my Fates,
>   And if she is sitting let her stand
>   And if she is standing let her come
>   And bring me a dream this night
>   Of the man I'm to marry."

That night, if the girl were virtuous, the Fates would hear her prayer. In her sleep, her Unknown God would come to her. He would stand by her bed, so close that she could see his face. Now at last, he would be known to her, the unknown visitor from her future. He might be someone she knew or he might be a stranger. But whoever he was, she would not be afraid as he bent over her, for he would be smiling in a kindly way and she would know at last that this was the man she would marry: this was the man she would belong to the rest of her life. He would take her by the red ribbon around her waist, and she would feel herself drawn toward him, drawn by a power beyond herself. She would

° A dry Kasiot doughnut made of barley flour.

see his face, smiling at her, and she would hear his voice whispering to her as soft as milk: "Let us go together now and reap the
harvest you have sown."

All this the custom of the island had ordained. The next day,
in the courtyards of the island, each girl proclaimed her vision,
according to the custom.

"I saw him," she would say.

"Did you? And what did he do?"

"He stood over me, at the foot of my bed."

"And then?"

"He bent over me, and drew me to him by the red cord around
my waist."

"And then?"

"He said, 'Let us go together now and reap the harvest you
have sown.'"

"And then?"

"And then . . . I don't know. . . . nothing."

"Nothing?"

"There isn't any more, is there? I mean . . . I don't remember
anything. I suppose I must have woke up."

Every girl had seen exactly what the custom ordained, nothing more or less. Each girl doubted the visions of the others and
became angry when she in turn was doubted. No matter how
faithfully the girls performed the ritual, there was no certainty
or conviction among them.

And then, one year, a Kasiot girl saw something different, and
among the maidens of the island, that vision became a legend.

The girl was named Katina, and she lived in a white gypsum
fortress near the top of the town of Poli, high on a hill among
the surrounding mountains. That year, her older sister Sofia had
been married, and the "speechless water" was set on the rooftop
of their house.

It was only by chance that Sofia and her husband happened to
be in Kasos. He was a captain who lived in Syros, and after she

married, Sofia had gone to live on that island two hundred miles away. They were only visiting in Kasos, on their way to Alexandria. The captain's ship was anchored in the lee of Makra Island, and they were staying a few days at Sofia's house in Poli.

Katina moved out of her room so the visitors could sleep there. She usually slept in the *moussandra*, a little attic above a ladder and a trap-door, where Katina's mother and father used to sleep. Her father had died several years before, and now that Sofia was married, Katina slept in the *moussandra* herself. Katina liked it, because it was far away from where every one else was sleeping, and when the trap-door was closed, her mother couldn't hear her and didn't know what time she went to sleep. But when Sofia and her husband came home to visit, Katina's mother decided that they should sleep in the *moussandra*.

"They need a quieter place to sleep," she explained to Katina, and so Katina gave up her room and took her clothes and things to a little alcove off the living room where the maid Maria usually slept. The maid Maria, in turn, was sent to stay with her cousin in Panayia.

At first, Katina didn't mind doing a favor for her older sister. Sofia had not been home all winter, and she was only staying a few days. But that was before Katina realized how proud and boastful her older sister had become. Ever since her wedding, Sofia pretended to be superior to Katina and all the other girls of Poli, just because she was married. Syros was not like Kasos at all, Sofia said, but a big city where ships came from all over the world, and the city square was so big that hundreds of people could walk back and forth on it. In Syros, Sofia explained, you didn't say good morning to everyone the way you did in Kasos, only to certain people, otherwise they would think you had no upbringing.

Now Katina began to resent her older sister. She hated the way everyone had to fuss over her just because she was married. When the "speechless water" was taken down from the roof,

Sofia was the only woman in the village not to sit on a cushion
on the courtyard floor and sing the *mandinadhas*. Instead, she
sat in an armchair on the upper terrace, looking down at everyone else, as though she were not part of the ceremony at all. Beside her, in another armchair, sat the captain, a great deal older
than Sofia, supposed to be very intelligent, though Katina had
never heard him say anything except, "The weather in Kasos is
truly magnificent, let us thank God for such a glorious day!" The
two of them sat in their armchairs on the upper terrace like a
king and queen, and after each *mandinadha* had been sung and
the fruit to go with it had been drawn up, Sofia would glance at
her husband, who was pulling gravely on his pipe, and then she
would catch his eye and smile at him.

That made Katina so furious that later that night, she asked
Sofia why she made fun of everything in Kasos. Why did she
make fun of the feast of *Kleithona*? Didn't she believe in it, or
in the Unknown God?

"I did once," Sofia said, hissing with laughter. "But now, why
should I? Now that I'm married."

With that, Sofia swaggered off to the quiet bedroom, leaving
Katina in tears of shame and anger.

That night, Katina put on her nightgown, tied the red ribbon
around her waist, and took two handfuls of barley, and a sip of
"speechless water." Then, in the center of the courtyard, her
cheeks still burning with her sister's laughter, she whirled as
fast as a dervish and scattered her barley to the four winds. That
night, as she set her head against the pillow, she prayed to her
Fates, as fervently as ever anyone had prayed to anyone in the
pantheon of the islands.

And Katina must truly have been a virtuous girl, because her
prayers were answered. Hardly an hour had passed since she
had drunk the Karpathian wine and ate the salt *koulouri*, the
communion gifts of this particular deity; and then while she was
still awake, the god himself appeared to her, not in a dream as

he appeared to other girls, but incarnate, a word become flesh.

She was lying awake, her face to the wall. Her eyes were tracing the curls and windings of a panel of arabesques below the ceiling. Suddenly, she became aware that the room was glowing with an unknown light. At first she thought it was the votive candles before the icons. But the icons were beyond the screen in the living room and this light was in the alcove itself, growing steadily brighter, like the flame in a kerosene lantern when you raised the wick. She turned over, and then suddenly she saw him standing over her: his head and shoulders framed in the window by her bed, a candle held before his face. In that one instant, she saw him perfectly, his face silent as an icon, the candlelight around his head like the halo of an archangel. She sat up in bed and gave a tiny cry of fright and wonder—she couldn't help it —and with that, the candle streaked away in an instant, like a falling star. The man vanished as suddenly as he appeared, and that window of her future, so miraculously illuminated, was darkened once again, enclosing nothing but a branch of bougainvillaea and a patch of moonless sky.

The next morning, Katina announced her vision to her girl friends.

"I saw him."

"Did you? What happened?"

"He stood outside my window, holding a candle to light his way."

"He *did*?" cried the other girl. "Is that what you dreamed?"

"No, I didn't dream it," Katina said. "I saw him. I was still awake when he came and stood at the window by my bed and held a candle in front of him."

"Impossible," said the other girl, astounded. "No one has ever dreamed of that before."

"I don't care what other people dream." Katina said. "I told you, I didn't dream it. I actually saw him, standing at the window by my bed."

"It cannot be," murmured a dozen voices, but without conviction. The idea was just beginning to grow on them that it might be possible. And if it were, these girls were thinking for the first time, then the custom of the island wouldn't make any difference. It absolutely wouldn't matter what anyone had dreamed before.

But for every visionary, there are seven skeptics. That is not a Kasiot saying, but it ought to be. Living with Katina and her mother in the white gypsum fortress were seven sisters of Katina's grandmother: seven black-cowled maidens who had ruled that threshold since anyone could remember. They had come when their older sister married Katina's grandfather, a solemn procession of seven sisters of the bride, accompanying the newly married couple as inevitably as the trousseau or dowry. They lived there, long after their Pure Monday, the first day of Lent when urchins of the village attached padlocks to the doors of all conspicuously unmarried women, signifying that their time of marriage was locked away. They were still there when Katina's mother was born, there again when Katina's grandmother died, there when Sofia and Katina arrived. On that threshold, they had become an eternal seven, ushering in all arrivals and departures.

It was Sofia who brought them out into the courtyard. Now it was Sofia who resented her sister's sudden popularity. She decided to put a stop to it, and to Katina's famous vision. In her guile, Sofia reasoned that if anyone would be inclined to disbelieve Katina's story, it would be her seven aunts. If there were anyone likely to mistrust Katina's vision, it would be these ladies, seven maidens who in seven decades, had received no gods of any sort, even in their dreams.

One by one, Sofia routed them out of the cracks and crevices where they lived, two from the cook-house, two more from another little house, three more from the storeroom where the grain and vegetables were kept. They came out in order of seniority: Anezoulla, Erinoulla, Evdoukoulla, Marigoulla, Zografoulla, Mangafoulla, and Mertianoulla. Tapping their canes and shuffling their slippers on the pebbled floor, they reclaimed their dominion of the courtyard.

"Katina saw her future husband!" announced the girls of Poli with one voice. "Not in a dream. But actually, standing at the window by her bed!"

"Indeed?" said Anezoulla, in her cackling voice.

"Impossible," said Erinoulla, in hers.

"She only dreamed of him," said Evdoukoulla, Marigoulla, and Zografoulla, at the same time.

"She only thought she saw him," said Mangafoulla and Mertianoulla.

"No, she saw him! She saw him!" cried all the girls of Poli.

"All right, in that case," said Anezoulla, raising her cane, "out of here, all of you." And with that, the court of inquiry was cleared of any maiden under sixty, except for the defendant.

Seven black-robed judges drew up their stools and brought Katina before them with all the gravity of inquisitors. Meanwhile, banished from the couryards, the girls of Poli peeped silently above the walls.

"In your own words, child," said Anezoulla, in a voice that was all patience and condescension, "tell us what happened."

"I was trying to go to sleep, "Katina said, "when suddenly I noticed there was a light in the room, and I turned over to see who was there, and then I saw my future husband standing in the window."

"And what did he look like?"

"I couldn't see his face, because he was holding a candle right in front of it."

"And what happened, child?"

"I was frightened and I cried out, and then suddenly he disappeared."

A murmur passed around that shrouded crescent. Adjusting their hoods of office, the judges resumed their inquiry.

"In your own words, child," said Erinoulla, imitating her sister. "Earlier last night, did you do everything according to the custom?"

Katina nodded.

"What did you do?"

"I spread the barley seed to the four winds, and I put the red ribbon around my waist, and then I went to bed."

"And then?"

"And then I drank the rest of the 'speechless water' and a glass of wine and I ate a salt *koulouri* and then . . ."

"And then you went to sleep," said Evdokoulla suddenly.

"That's right."

"Aha! Aha!" cried the black inquisitor, shaking her stick. "You see? You went to sleep, and in your *sleep*, the man appeared to you."

"No! No!" Katina said. "You're trying to confuse me. I didn't go to sleep, I went to *bed,* and I lay awake for maybe an hour or so, and then I saw him in the window."

"But how do you know you weren't asleep?"

"Because I wasn't."

"But it could have been a dream."

"It could have been, but it wasn't."

"But how do you know?"

"Because I wasn't asleep. You cannot dream if you aren't asleep."

Another murmur passed around the circle. On the ramparts of the courtyard, the girls of Poli chattered happily.

"Silence!" cried Anezoulla, raising a slipper. Instantly a dozen faces sank below the courtyard wall.

Turning back to the defendant, Anezoulla tried another approach.

"Tell us child," she said. "Did you pray to the Fates, according to the custom?"

"Yes."

"And what did you say?"

"I said the prayer I had learned."

"Yes, child, but what was it. How did it go?"

"You want me to say it for you now?"

"Yes, child, we want you to say it for us now."

Katina said the prayer, her hands twisting behind her back just as they did in school when she had to stand up before the whole class and recite the "Our Father." But she got through it without a mistake.

"Just a moment! What did you say, child?" said Anezoulla. "Say those the last four lines again."

> "And if she is sitting let her stand,
> And if she is standing let her come.
> And bring me a dream this night
> Of the man I'm to marry."

"And bring you a *dream* of the man you're to marry. And bring you a *dream* of him, my child. You asked the Fates to make you dream of him, and that is just what they did. You went to sleep and *dreamed* you saw the man you're going to marry."

"Oh, you don't *want* to believe me," cried Katina with tears in her eyes.

"There, there, it doesn't matter," said Mertianoulla, the youngest sister, putting her arms around Katina. "If you dreamed of him, it's all the same. If you dreamed of the man you're going to marry, you're a very lucky girl."

"That's right," said Mangafoulla. "You dreamed of the man you're going to marry. What more can you ask for?"

"That's right, that's right," echoed other cackling voices. "What more can you ask for?"

Katina stopped crying. Around the courtroom, the shrouded judges watched her. At the walls, the girls of Poli waited, to see if Katina would go back on what she said.

But she did not. The Maid did not recant. The Maid was

obdurate. She wiped her eyes, and in a cool voice, confirmed in heresy, she said, "I did not *dream* of him. I was awake when he came to me, and I saw him with my own eyes."

Now Katina's doom was sealed. Not even kindly Merti-anoulla could save her now. Anezoulla rose off her stool, pointing a bony finger. Around her, a final time, judges adjusted hoods of office.

"One more thing, child," said Anezoulla. "Did he speak to you, this man?"

Katina shook her head.

"He didn't say anything?"

"No."

"Well that is very strange, child," said Anezoulla, smiling so cunningly now that Katina began to feel uneasy.

"Very strange indeed, since it has been known for generations that on the night of *Kleithona,* a young maiden is visited in her sleep by the man she will marry, and he draws her to him by the red cord around her waist, and says to her in a voice as soft as milk: "Let us go together now and reap the harvest you have sown. You remember that, my child?"

Katina nodded.

"But he didn't say that to you?"

Katina shook her head.

"I wonder if you can explain that to us, child. I wonder if you can tell us why he didn't say that, why he didn't speak to you."

Katina didn't answer.

Anezoulla waited, her arms folded in her black sleeves. Around her, the judges waited. On the parapets, the girls of Poli waited. But this time, Katina had no answer. A dreadful silence had fallen on the courtyard. The Maid of Poli had nothing to say.

"Well, perhaps *I* can explain it to *you,*" Anezoulla said. "If you had told us that you went to sleep last night and *dreamed* that your future husband stood over you and drew you to him and spoke to you in a voice as soft as milk. . . . we would have believed you. Many girls on the island have dreamed the same. But instead you tell us that you were not asleep, that you saw him with your own eyes. And that, of course, is the answer in itself. That itself is the reason he did not speak to you."

Six judges looked at Anezoulla, wondering what she had in mind.

"What do you mean?" said Katina.

"What do I mean? I'll tell you what I mean. According to the custom of the island, a girl must be asleep when her future husband comes by her bed. When your future husband came to draw you toward him by the red cord of maidenhood around your waist, he should have found you with your eyelids closed, seeing him in your dreams. But instead, he found you awake, as you admit. When he appeared at your window, you sat up in bed and screamed at him. And he must have thought 'What kind of girl is this? She is supposed to be asleep, according to the custom of the island, but instead, she sits up in bed and screams at me. This girl I do not want for a wife. I will go away now and find another girl.'"

And at this devious reasoning, the solemn court of inquiry started cackling and hissing. Seven judges trembled in arid, toothless laughter.

Tears were streaming down Katina's cheeks; her face was burning with anger and frustration. There was nothing she could do, nothing she could say to these seven wicked judges, rocking on their stools. Even her companions could not help her now, watching from the parapets.

She ran to her room, and lay down on her bed behind the screen, the only place where she could be alone. And beside the vacant window and the bougainvillaea, she wept tears of loneliness. Now Anezoulla's dry cackling laughter came back to her. Why hadn't her future husband spoken to her? Why hadn't he said "Let us go together and reap the harvest you have sown." Could it be true, what her aunt had said?

Katina thought it must be true. There would be no husband for her. All her friends would marry, one by one, and only she would be left alone. A Pure Monday would come when she would awake to find a padlock fastened to her door, and all the urchins of the island laughing at her.

Now, lonely and despairing, Katina wept herself to sleep, praying to the Fates to give her some sign, to prove that it wasn't true what Anezoulla had said, that she wouldn't have a husband.

Then the miracle happened. The Fates heard her prayer and answered it. Once again, she knew it was not a dream. She woke up on her lonely cot, the tears flowing again as soon as she remembered what had happened. She got up and went to the window, and looked out into the little garden at the rear of the house where the bougainvillaea was blooming, wine-red against the gypsum walls. And there, through her tears, Katina caught sight of something on the pebbled courtyard floor.

She ran outside to have a closer look, and on the pebbles, she saw a neat red spot. It had flowed down neatly over three pebbles, settling into the cracks between them, so that they looked like tiny eggs, dyed red for Easter. And now Katina had her sign, evidence to prove her aunt was wrong. Dried and clinging to the pebbles beneath her window was a spot of red wax: the drippings of the candle the Unknown God had held.

"You see! You see!" Katina cried, though there was no one there to see. Before the shuttered windows, where the seven judges had crawled off into their shady cracks to doze away the hours of the afternoon, Katina danced and shouted.

"Come and see!" she cried. "Come and see!"

One by one, the seven guardians came out, two from the

cook-house, two more from the other little house, another three from the storeroom where the dried fruits and vegetables were kept. Out they came, the hobbling storm-troops for moral emergency.

"You see! You see!" cried Katina, dancing and shouting. Seven black theologians stooped over the spot of wax.

"*Kyrie Eleison!*" said Anezoulla, making the sign of the cross. "God the Father protect us!"

"And God the Son!" said Erinoulla.

"And God the Holy Ghost!" said the rest, in chorus.

The black chorus fell to their knees and made the sign of the cross as though they thought the earth would open at their feet. In a few minutes, all the girls of Poli were in Katina's courtyard, dancing in victory. Katina had seen her future husband, not in a dream, but actually, standing at the window by her bed. Among the maidens of the island, Katina's vision was proclaimed a miracle, and her story became a legend.

Of course, her miracle has an explanation, like all miracles. But if anyone prefers it—if anyone of little faith prefers a reason to a miracle—let him draw up his stool and take his place with the black-cowled sophists whose gods have failed. Even they, curiously, did not prefer the reason. At the last moment, even the sharp-tongued sisters kept a cross upon their lips, choosing to celebrate a Maid's miracle instead of the dishonor of a maid.

Anezoulla realized it first. She passed the secret on to Erinoulla, who passed it on to Evoudkoulla and on to Marigoulla, Zografoulla, Mangafoulla, and Mertianoulla. From shrouded mouth to shrouded ear, the riddle of the Unknown Deity was undone.

Anezoulla remembered that on the night of *Kleithona*, Katina was not sleeping in the *moussandra*. She was sleeping in that alcove off the living room where the maid Maria should have slept. So the miracle could be explained, after all.

Katina had told the truth. A man had come and stood in the window by her bed, holding a candle to light his way, and it was true Katina had been awake when she saw him. But this man had not come for Katina, not at all. He had not come for the Maid of Poli, but for Maria the maid; and he could have been coming with miraculous regularity, though unlike Katina, Maria had felt no need to boast about it.

In that way, even an Unknown God could be explained. But the seven sisters did not explain him. Instead they adjusted their hoods of office once again, took up their walking sticks, and marched down the road from Poli to Panayia. Within the hour, while there was still a shaving of the sun above Armathia Island, a stern tribunal was convened to hear another case. In a courtyard in Panayia, a second defendant was brought before them and a second verdict was pronounced. The maid Maria was turned out forever from their gypsum fortress and sent out homeless onto the island. That feast of *Kleithona*, she became the only maid in Kasos who did not rejoice at the discovery of her Unknown God.

A
Feast of
Vengeance

"*I* hear you are writing a book about Kasos," someone said to me at a cocktail party in New York. "I hope you are going to include the story of my great-grandmother. She had an innocent man executed to avenge her husband's death, and when the executioner cut off his head, she raised the sword to her lips and drank her victim's blood."

He was wrong. His great-grandmother had not drunk her victim's blood. The sword was passed to her before the execution, not afterward. The blood-drinking is spurious, made up sometime in the century that followed the event, and it only shows how the woman's descendants hold her in awe.

I first heard the story in my childhood.

"She was a true virago," I heard Uncle George say, "who would stop at nothing to have her vengeance. Pity and justice meant nothing to her, and she took her vengeance on an innocent man, concluding a vendetta."

Of that occasion in my childhood, I remember only those

words heard for the first time: virago, vendetta. They were unfamiliar combinations of syllables which could be pronounced in English, but whose meaning seemed locked in some other language yet unknown. They had a ring of terror about them, but also a ring of exultation: A virago must be a wild, wicked woman, and Vendetta might have been the woman's name.

Years later, I got Uncle George to tell me the story again. By that time, I had learned that vendetta is not a woman's name, but an honored ceremony based on the principle of a life for a life. In addition, according to a book I read, vendetta has something to do with the fear of vampires. The ancient Greeks believed that if a man was murdered and his death was not avenged, his body would not decompose in the grave and he would rise to haunt the living. Although this belief originated with the ancients, ever since the Slavic migrations, the phenomenon has had a Slavic name—*vrykolakas*—and in behavior, he has resembled the Slavic vampire: rising from the grave to feed on the living, his own family first of all.

Ever since his arrival, the *vrykolakas* has made tracks across the mind of Greece. He has risen every night but Saturday from graveyards all over the country, his body full as a wine-skin and tight as a drum. Whenever many deaths occurred in rapid succession, villagers would suspect a *vrykolakas* among their dead. The next Saturday, accompanied by the priest, they would gather in the graveyard to dig up graves. If they found a body that had not decomposed—one with nails and hair and flesh— that man was the *vrykolakas*. The priest would say a prayer over him, an exorcism devised especially by the church; and if he did not decompose at once, the priest would allow the villagers to burn him, or cut out his heart and boil it in vinegar.

In Greece, even now, the relationship between the living and the dead is a very solemn one. The period of mourning lasts officially for three years, and in rural areas, it is observed so strictly that mourners may not be seen at any public celebration until the three years are over. During that time, at given intervals, the Orthodox religion prescribes memorial services to be held for the repose of the deceased. Friends and family assemble in the church. The priests bless a sort of honey-cake and a paste called *kolyva* made of boiled wheat, honey, pomegranate seeds, nuts, and raisins. After the ceremony, these sweatmeats are passed around the congregation and shared in the dead man's memory.

These services are probably remnants of certain pagan feasts connected with the same fear of resuscitation. The ancients believed that a man would also rise from the grave if he had died under a curse. To guard against this danger, they devised the custom of inviting all a dead man's friends and relatives to share a feast in his honor, hoping that in the conviviality of the occasion, any curses held against him would be loosened. The pagan feasts were held at the same intervals after death as some of the Orthodox memorials. In addition, because of the scarcity of burial land in Greece, it has been customary to exhume the body after three years and place the remains in an ossuary. Since there can be no fear that a body will turn into a *vrykolakas* after it is exhumed, the danger of resuscitation exits only during the first three years. And here the connection between the memorials and the *vrykolakas* becomes most obvious. The last memorial is conducted on the third anniversary of the death, when the body is exhumed and the fear of the *vrykolakas* is forever ended.

Both vendettas and memorials are responses to the fear of the *vrykolakas*. In that sense, the execution of a man who pleaded for mercy with his dying breath can be taken as a sort of religious ceremony in itself, analogous to an offering of *kolvya* and honey-cakes. Like the sea on shores very far removed from the center of a storm, the memorials of the present day are gentle waves spreading outward from a storm of terror and compulsion which nearer to the center, in the past, resulted in vendettas such as the death of the virago's victim.

The Virago was my great-great-grandmother, the mother of Old Yia-Yia; Old-Old-Yia-Yia, we must call her, following Eddie's formula. Her husband, Hazimanolis Malliarakis, was the one who built the house of the blue shutters and the one next to it for his eldest two daughters, Marigo and another one who died without children. There, in the house next door, is where the tale begins. When the second daughter died without an heir, according to the custom, the house reverted to the family and was awarded finally to Eleni. By the time I arrived in Kasos in 1964, the house had crumbled into ruins, but in Uncle George's childhood, it was in perfect condition, with people living in it: a couple from Karpathos and their daughter who was Eleni's god-child.

They were poor people; the father had a little boat which he used to shuttle gypsum from Armathia Island to the ships anchored at Makra. The little girl's name was Evamorphia; she was the same age as Uncle George, and they used to play together in the abandoned foundations and plots around the neighborhood. They collected pieces of broken crockery from empty houses and pretended they were pieces of money, with a given value according to the size.

Once George wanted to buy a plate of figs, and he offered Evamorphia a huge fragment unearthed with great care from some foundation.

"I haven't any change," he said, drawing out the fragment ostentatiously.

But if Evamorphia was impressed, she concealed the fact.

"Haven't any change?" she said. "Well, give it here. I'll change it for you."

With that, she took George's piece of pottery and dropped it on the stones at his feet.

"There you are," she said, while George stared at the hundreds of pieces. "There's your change."

But soon enough, such neighborhood games were at an end, and George lost his Evamorphia. That was Old Yia-Yia's fault, for she was very quarrelsome and vengeful. She had a fight with Evamorphia's mother, and the next day, she decided that if that family were to live next door, they would have to pay rent. That was impossible: they could not afford it, and Eleni would never have thought of such a thing because these people were her friends. But Old Yia-Yia was intransigent. The rent must be paid: one could not give up a house for nothing. And so Evamorphia and her parents moved away. That is why the house next door was ruined. Evamorphia's mother had kept it spotlessly clean, and coated it with gypsum in the spring and fall. But now, with no one living in it, the house soon fell to pieces.

George was inconsolable, sitting on the wall watching Evamorphia and her parents packing their belongings. But he could not express his sorrow or Old Yia-Yia would have beaten him. (She was a fierce woman and used to beat her grandsons, just for amusement.) He kept all his injury inside, and one day unexpectedly, it came out. He saw Evamorphia's mother in the street in Phry and called out an obscenity to her, as though she, poor woman, were to blame.

Evamorphia's mother replied coolly, with an epigram. "With whatever teacher you sit down," she said, "that's the lesson you will learn."

And that was very appropriate, for whatever obscenity it had been, George had learned it from Old Yia-Yia. But what George did not know was that the saying held true for grown-ups as well as children. At one time or other, Old Yia-Yia herself had sat down with some teacher of her own. Old Yia-Yia had had a mother too, though as a child George would never have suspected it. And it was Old Yia-Yia's mother, the Virago, who had taught her all the curses she would ever need. For not only had she brought an innocent man to be executed before her children's eyes, but on his way to the scaffold, she outdid him in cursing.

But George knew nothing of the Virago at the time. He had heard nothing of the story, and he did not even know of his great-grandfather, Hazimanolis Malliarakis, until that afternoon when Evamorphia and her parents had departed.

He wandered next door, trying to console himself for his loss; he scavenged about in the leavings of that abandoned house and emerged with relics of the former owner's life which caused his grandmother to speak her father's name and eventually to tell the story of his assassination in Alexandria and the subsequent execution in Rhodes. Until then, George had heard nothing of Hazimanolis, had not even heard of anyone named Hazimanolis or Hazi-Anybody, and did not even know that Hazi is a prefix added to a Christian name which indicates—in imitation of the Moslems who call themselves *Hadji* after they have made the pilgrimage to Mecca—that the bearer has made a Christian pilgrimage to Jerusalem and been baptised in the Jordan River. George did not yet know that afternoon that the name Hazimanolis means The Pilgrim Manuel, signifying that the bearer had gone to the Holy City of Jerusalem sometime before he made the final journey to Alexandria, the city of his death.

Venturing into that house next door, vacant for the first time since he could remember, George made certain discoveries. First, he found wedding chests and broken crockery; then he found the *tsimbouks*, those relics not of his grandfather's but his great-grandfather's generation, for by the time Old Yia-Yia married Vasilios no one smoked *tsimbouks* in Kasos and they had become relics of a former life that had to be dug up out of abandoned houses to be seen.

They even looked like relics: long pipes made of bone, lying in the bottom of the wedding chest like bones in a coffin, peaceable remains exhumed on the third anniversary of interment.

But George was unearthing them decades after the last memorial for Hazimanolis had been sung, almost a half a century after the phantoms of the Virago's heart had been laid to rest forever, not by any offering of *kolyva* and honey-cakes but by a feast of vengeance.

To George, that day in Kasos, they suggested no such thing as relics, for he knew nothing of Hazimanolis and sought no *hapari* of him during that afternoon's researches. The only connection they could have had to that unknown event in Alexandria was that George discovered them exactly at the time he discovered vengeance. In his solitude, he wandered aimlessly in the house next door, and straightaway discovered the *tsimbouks*, as though the very rancor of his heart had summoned them out of the cavernous, smiling jaws of the old wedding chest.

At once he imagined them as weapons: long pointed lances. One by one he fastened them to the end of a wooden pole and thrust them in desperate, purposeless revenge against the wall of that now forever empty house. By the time he was interrupted, he had broken every one of them. At sundown his grandmother found him raging like a crazy dwarf, his lance raised against an empty wall, thrusting at the faceless phantoms of his heart.

That was when he first heard of his great-grandfather, for when his grandmother saw him she threw up her hands and said, "You hear? You hear?" (She always used this expression to nurse a growing wrath, though in itself it meant nothing.) "What are you doing there?" And George stopped, frozen. Grandmother saw it was a *tsimbouk* he had fastened to the end of a pole, and she said, "You hear? You hear? Where did you find that?" George pointed to the house next door, and then at once his grandmother understood, that he had unearthed them from that house which her father had built sometime before he sailed away on his last pilgrimage, before that day when he went ashore after sunset and ventured into an impenetrable fog to keep an appointment with the Kikos family, several gentlemen who stepped around him from the mists and greeted him unusually politely considering their intent: "Good evening, Hazimanoli."

Much later, Old Yia-Yia told the full story to Uncle George, to my father, and to her other grandsons. She told it every time they asked her, which might be every time they sat through an evening together, first in the house in Syros, then in Wembley Park in London. Up to 1935, eighty-five years after that execution in Rhodes, Marigo, outrageously, was still telling the story. She would walk around Wembley in her black cowl, and sometimes she would get lost going from one grandson's house to another, so that they would have to go out to retrieve her. In these days, she had begun to lose her grasp on the world, and hearing all her grandsons talking to their mother, she would call Eleni mother too.

"She's not your mother," someone would explain, "she's your daughter." And Old Yia-Yia would grapple with such concepts as time and generations which by then had become almost meaningless and say, "You mean I don't have a mother anymore?"

But in spite of that, she never forgot what her mother had done, and what happened on the square in Rhodes when she was a girl of eight.

The Kikos family had a widow sister, as Old Yia-Yia told her grandsons, and Hazimanolis had a brother who was having an affair with her. That was the cause of the catastrophe. Hazimanolis was the eldest in his family. His brother's name was Hazimalliaras: Hazi because he was a brother of Hazimanolis and the relatives and descendants of pilgrims were called Hazi too, and Malliaras (hairy, hirsute) as a nickname, because he had a thick blond hair and his chest and arms were hairy.°

° If you were to translate his name literally into English, as some Greeks do when they arrive in America, you would have to call him The Pilgrim's Hairy Brother. But I think it is better to call him Hazimalliaras.

There were rumors that Hazimalliaras would marry the widow, and as head of his family, Hazimanolis decided to put a stop to the affair. He intervened, not with his brother, but with the Kikos family. (Hazimalliaras himself plays a small role in the story, though like Helen, he launched the ships.) The Kikos' owed Hazimanolis money, a sum they could not pay. If they did not tell their sister to stop her designs, Hazimanolis threatened to present their promissory note when it fell due and arrest their ship in payment.

The Kikos' were outraged. To spite Hazimanolis, they courted Hazimalliaras more openly than ever. And for his part, as he promised, Hazimanolis sailed to Alexandria, where the note had been signed and therefore had to be presented. Thus it happened that Hazimanolis arrived in Alexandria, sometime around 1850.

With him sailed Mavrandonis, who later became Captain Elias' first mate. Once when he was discussing the matter with Old Yia-Yia in George's hearing, he told her the story of her father's murder.

He said the fog that night was so thick you couldn't see your feet. The ship was moored in the harbor of Alexandria, and after dinner, Hazimanolis wanted to go ashore, and Mavrandonis and two other sailors rowed him in the lifeboat. The sailors rowed slowly, picking their way among the gray forms looming in the fog and the anchor chains and moorings set out in diagonals across their course. Mavrandonis was not rowing perhaps, but sitting in the bows, calling out instructions in a voice that must have seemed unusually loud and clear on a night when you might imagine you could hear as poorly as you could see; incongruously enough, the voice could probably be heard across the harbor, perhaps even by the conspirators already assembled on the shore. And in the stern sat the captain, unbending, resolute, borne on silently to his death.

He was a quick man, but even so, for him to have had time to draw his walking stick, he must have known what was up as soon as he saw the shapes emerging from the darkness. He must have known who they were and what they intended as soon as he heard the spokesman give the signal by addressing him in a voice that was unusually composed and dignified considering first the errand and secondly the fact that in a fog that thick you would expect a man to shout to make himself heard. But he didn't shout, this unknown spokesman. He only said "good evening," timing this greeting to the slight increase in the loudness of Hazimanolis' steps and the muffled tapping of the cane on the muddy Arab street. Then, at the proper moment, when the spokesman stepped forward to say good evening (a greeting appropriate enough, except that in this case the evening would last for all eternity), without motion of their own, the surrounding forms sprang into being. Almost the same instant Hazimanolis raised his Malacca walking stick with the silver handle, and with his other hand he took hold of the lower end, pulled his two arms asunder as though to break bonds, and stripped the cane of its wooden sheathing to reveal a razor-sharp, twenty-five-inch blade.

But Hazimanolis was not quick enough. No man could have been, to stride unsuspecting into that ambuscade and still survive. The spokesman had just stepped forward to make his greeting, and Hazimanolis was just preparing a reply to it— a twenty-five-inch piece of steel. And then, no more than an instant later, a man fell on Hazimanolis from the rear and thrust his own pointed and laconic message an inch or two below the Captain's neck. (We don't even know who it was, since it was not he, almost a year later, who suffered retribution on the square in Rhodes.) And all this happened before the spokesman had finished. All he had said by that time was "good evening" and then there was that brief, steely interchange, and then, looking down at a man forever silenced by his feet, he said, "Hazimanolis," addressing a corpse by name.

"They've killed your captain," cried a sailor, running past

Mavrandonis and the other men waiting at the landing. They ran and found the captain, dead in the street, hardly a hundred yards from safety. At sunrise, the story came to light. The city was revealed like a face before a veil, and emerging from the obscurity of night and fog, the rigging of all the Kasiot ships appeared in an insignia of death as unmistakable as a woman's parted hair. The yards were crossed in mourning, black and naked against the sky, including the yards of the Kikos' ship, in a shameless travesty of the custom.

The Kikos' were all arrested, for every Kasiot in Alexandria knew of the debt they owed the dead captain and the grudge. A lawyer advised them to nominate one of their number to confess the crime. (Under Ottoman law, the only guilty one was the one whose blow caused death). And that is how they came to nominate not the murderer himself but his younger brother Basil. They expected he would have to spend a month or two in prison and then would be set free. And they chose him because unlike his elder brother—the truly guilty one— he was unmarried and so would leave no wife and children temporarily deprived of a livelihood. That was what they said, though it is just possible that somewhere in the bottom of their minds, they may have been singling him out for a reason equally self-evident and persuasive though impossible to articulate, that at the conclusion of his term in prison, he would leave, deprived of livelihood on their native island, no widow and no orphans.

Now the Virago made her appearance on the scene. She arrived in Alexandria with her children and the maids, like country relatives in town for a cousin's wedding. There must have been an air of anticipation about her, a certain eagerness for the future inappropriate in a mourning widow. When you think of her, you do not think of someone in mourning. You can hardly imagine her with tears in her eyes. Instead, you have to think of all her actions as a kind of mourning, since grief and bereavement may be expressed in any form; but mourning in the strictest sense is the relationship between the living and the dead and so must be conducted according to established rules—the hair pulling and the memorials—and the way her mourning was expressed was by neither one, but by the vengeance. That is why I see the scene in Rhodes as a kind of feast, the offering on behalf of her husband's soul being no pie of dried wheat and honey but the body of an alleged murderer served up like *kolyva* with the name of the deceased written on it in the Virago's heart.

The Khedive of Egypt was in Alexandria then, listening to the grievances of his subjects. Miraculously, the Virago gained an audience with him. She gained it by a trick, by means of her pretty daughter, then a girl of eight. Late one afternoon, in the audience hall with the moorish portals, the Khedive was about to hear one more case. The guards had stepped inside to listen to his instructions, and the door was left unguarded. That moment, a little girl was pushed between the portals and padded across the marble floor as directly as she pads into her own story: Old Yia-Yia, at the age of eight.

"Who is this pretty child?" said Uncle George, quoting both the Khedive and his grandmother, as he retold the story himself.

"Who is this pretty child?" said Old Yia-Yia, quoting the Khedive as she told the story to her grandsons.

"Who is this pretty child?" the Khedive said himself, in Alexandria, in 1850. "Who is she and what does she want?"

The guards told him that she was the daughter of a Greek woman waiting outside, who demanded retribution for her husband's murder.

"Then let her enter," replied the Khedive in his kindly voice. "Hers is the last case we shall hear today."

In this way, the Virago brought her case before the Khedive of Egypt. Probably he had been told that the confessed murderer was really innocent, and he must have wanted to close the case as soon as possible. Anwyay, his reply was a masterpiece of conciliation.

"The Khedive suggests," said an interpreter, translating for the Virago, "that we should wait until this pretty girl is grown to be a woman. Then she can tell us whether the defendant should be punished."

But the Virago's reply made the smile vanish from the Khedive's face. "Rather than agree to such a thing," she said, "I would have my daughter's throat cut before my eyes and never see her grow to be a woman."

Now Basil's fate began to darken. The lawyer tried a different tactic. He claimed that since the defendant was a Turkish subject, he must be tried in Rhodes, in the court which had jurisdiction over Kasos. In this way, the lawyer hoped the Virago would not be able to afford more transportation and hotel bills and would have to give up her pursuit. But he underestimated her. She had spent all her dowry by that time, and now she appealed to the Malliarakis family, probably threatening them with the bloated specter of her dead husband rising to feed on them as well. In any case, the Malliarakis family provided the money (and ruined themselves in the process). And with this fatal assistance, on the heels of the lawyer and the Kikos family, the Virago and her breed of plaintiffs arrived in Rhodes.

The case was tried and Basil was found guilty by his own confession, but the Rhodian judges were no more anxious to have him executed than the Khedive had been. They invoked a law, providing that if any member of the plaintiff's family should grant mercy to the accused, his sentence would be commuted and his life would be spared. What they were hoping, of course, was that if the Virago's children were ordered to be present at the execution, in the horror of the spectacle one of them might cry out for mercy. They ordered the Virago to bring them to the execution, as though it were a wedding or a christening. The children would stand with her below the scaffold, and if the head of this innocent man were to roll tomorrow, the children would be there to see it roll: unless she wished to spare them the horror of such a spectacle and grant him mercy now herself. Would she grant mercy to the defendant?

"I grant him nothing," the Virago said, "and neither will my children."

"Then a good night to you," the judges answered, "and a good night to your children."

Everyone went away to prepare for the next day, the Virago and her children to their new hotel, the Kikos brothers and the lawyers to visit Basil in the dungeon. The attendants must have been erecting the wooden scaffolding in the square where the next day the whole population of the city would gather as though around an arena stage. The Virago must have been giving her children their final coaching, saying, "He will ask you for mercy. He will ask you to spare his life. But whatever he says, you are not to speak to him. They will show you the sword they will use to cut off his head, and if you say a word, they will use that blade to cut your heads off instead."

In another part of the city, in the dungeon, the Kikos brothers and the lawyer must have sat with Basil, the lawyer saying, "Remember the children. The children will be the ones to save you. You must kneel down before them until one of them grants you mercy. That way your life will be saved."

Basil Kikos must have listened to his instructions without paying much attention, not comprehending the danger he was in. The agreement was that if he would confess the crime, his brothers and the lawyer would see that he went free. He had done his part; the rest he left to them. Even now, when his hopes had dwindled until they rested with half a dozen little children, still he did not think of death—still it was the furthest matter from his mind.

But not one of the brothers looked at any of the others, as they sat with Basil on his final night.

As for the other brother, the real murderer, we know nothing about him, or his feelings. Old Yia-Yia never seemed to have been troubled by the question, never even learned the man's name. From what we know of Kasiot families, we can suppose if the man had been anywhere on earth that night, he would have been in that prison with his brother. Maybe he *was* sitting with all the other brothers, on a stool the obliging Turks had brought for him, unable to look any of the others in the eye, trying to believe as this boastful Basil evidently believed that there was no fear of death.

Then, the next morning, perhaps he had been about to cry out, or break out of the crowd and up the scaffold, when the inexorable collective judgment of a Kasiot family reached out to stop him: a Kikos hand clapped over his mouth, Kikos arms around him. Maybe he was carried off, struggling in muted protest, by those other Kikos brothers who reasoned instantly and with a god-like presumption that they had the right to make that choice, that since one Kikos had to die that day, let it be Basil, poor little Basil, who was the youngest and had not had time to take the crown and so would leave upon his native island no widow and no orphans.

Basil came out of prison suspecting nothing. The square was full of people—Greeks, Turks, and Jews—surrounding the scaffold like the sea. Basil was led up the steps. Then, in front of priests, judges, dignitaries of the Rhodian government, and almost the entire population of the city, the Virago outdid him in cursing.

"You hear? You hear?" she cried to the people surrounding her, employing a meaningless expletive she used habitually to nurse her wrath. "You hear? You hear?" she cried. "There he goes. There goes the foul cowardly villain. You hear? You hear?"

And then, before the instantly silent population of the city, Basil Kikos turned to confront his black antagonist.

"Old harlot," he called down to her. "When I am free, I will tie you in a foresail and throw you to the bottom of the sea so the sun will not shine on you."

And the Virago returned his wrath with interest, though even she did not taunt him with the fact—obvious to everyone except the one it touched most critically—that what he said was foolish because he would not go free except into his grave.

"Blaspheming villain," she replied. "May the plague take you and all your kinsmen. May they all follow you in a procession to the grave. May your mother kiss their foreheads in the casket after yours."

"And you, vile slattern," Kikos returned, groping for words to match her steady escalation of abuse. "May they take all your children away on the sheet. May they . . ."

But before he could go on, the widow bested him.

"The same to you and all who love you," she cried. "May the mother who bore you curse the day you were conceived. May the womb that carried you be eaten by the pox. And may the hand that cut your birth-cord burn in hell."

Basil Kikos turned away defeated, outdone in cursing by a woman. That moment, he had his first perception of what would happen. Turning away from the Virago, he saw two priests standing on the scaffold, darkening that sunny platform like shadows. Soundlessly, they moved toward him, one holding a gilded Bible, the other a spoon and a chalice.

Stepping backward, Basil shrank from them and an instant later, he received his second shock. Behind the priests he saw two more figures in black hoods, holding up the instruments of another calling: one the short, pointed sword, the other the long, curved, glistening one.

He stumbled backward down the steps again, almost into the Virago's arms.

"The children! The children!" shouted his brothers from the crowd.

Then, Basil remembered the instructions he had heard so often, and at last he understood them. In an instant, he forgot all the threats and curses he had heaped upon this family.

"Little boy," he said, to the first of the Virago's children, "have mercy on me."

But the little boy did not have mercy, or at least he did not show it, and Basil proceeded to the next child.

"Have mercy on me," he begged him, but this child was silent too.

Basil proceeded down the line of children, four boys and two girls standing beside their mother in that regular family phalanx, a solid chain forged of common fear: six terror-stricken children bound to silence. From one to the other, Basil crawled on his hands and knees. And in his frenzy he made it easier for them than it might have been. No sooner had one child refused him, but he crawled on, desperately, to the next one. In that way, he wasted them. In an instant, five of them were lost forever. Between him and death was a single, final child: a girl of eight.

With this one, he took more time.

"What's her name?" he cried, to the onlookers, standing by.

"Whoever told him," said Old Yia-Yia, more than half a century later, "it wasn't me, for I was so frightened I couldn't speak."

"Who it was we shall never know," said Uncle George, after another half a century. "Perhaps the lawyer or one of the Kikos brothers, or some Kasiot standing by who knew the Malliarakis family."

But apart from what Old Yia-Yia and Uncle George have said, I have a theory of my own. I believe the Virago told him. Who else could it have been, since she was standing right beside her daughter? What would have been more natural than for her mother to introduce her? Is there any reason why the Virago would not have responded to this question as any other mother would have, identified her child before the stranger, even straightened her hair a little, looking on with pride and love.

"What's her name?" cried Basil Kikos. "Will someone tell me this child's name?"

"Marigo," replied the Virago, like any other mother.

"Save me, Marigo," cried Basil. "Have mercy on me, and I shall be your slave for the rest of my life!"

But Marigo did not have mercy. A look from her mother quenched all mercy in her.

"Save me, Marigo," cried Basil again. "Grant mercy to me, and I will crawl ahead of you the rest of my days and lick the earth beneath your feet."

But this time the Virago intervened. "We grant you nothing, you worthless faggot,"* she said, and Basil Kikos turned away, put down again.

"The sword! The sword!" the judges cried. "Show it to the children. Children, unless you have mercy on this man, they will use this sword to cut off his head!"

And so they showed the sword to all the children, to those diminutive accomplices of the widow's vengeance. Before each one of them, they passed the broad, curved, glistening blade. They passed it around like a rare dish, carefully prepared, which must be approved by every one who will partake of it before it can be served. The children were paralyzed with fear, unable to look at each other, or at anything except this huge glistening blade. Still their tongues were frozen in their heads. Still they did not grant mercy, and so the guards passed the

---

* Uncle George wrote me this part of the story from his office in Piraeus. As Basil neared his execution, Uncle George was nearing the bottom of a page. His handwriting became smaller and smaller until, finally, this last word was indecipherable. "I could not read the word the Virago used," I wrote him in my next letter. Ten days later came this reply. "Strange you could not read the word. It was a bad word, very unsuitable in a woman's mouth. It was: FAGGOT."

blade to the Virago. It was a needless gesture, but since she had ordered that feast of vengeance, it was only fitting that she approve it. That was the incident which her great-grandson mentioned at the cocktail party in New York, when she lifted the sword to her enraptured lips. But it was before the execution, not afterward, and the only outrage she committed was against religion, not against nature.

"Blessed be this sword which brings me vengeance," she said, and kissed it as though it were an icon. Then, returning the sword to the executioners, she folded her hands upon her breast and watched the remainder of that spectacle in tranquillity.

Two guards at Basil's either arm led him back up the staircase to the scaffold. The priests advanced from opposite directions, one holding the gilded Bible, the other the chalice and the spoon. For a moment, Basil must have stopped his struggling to watch them. He must have watched the priest raise the chalice, and extend the spoon toward his mouth. For a single moment, Basil Kikos must have made no move except to open his mouth in that gesture of acceptance he had first made when he was a baby in his mother's arms. Now he opened his mouth again, and as the priest tipped the spoon upon his tongue, he had just time enough to wonder why they were giving him Communion, there on the scaffold where he was supposed to die. Then the next moment, the truth was in him: truth bursting out of mystery. For the first time he knew he was going to die. There with the Blood of his Redeemer in his mouth, he knew the truth. His mouth was full of it, full of the Truth, and he tasted the death in it, not the Eternal Life. As the two priests hovered in solicitation for his soul, crossing themselves and moaning a Litany for the dead, Basil cried out like a damned soul in descent to hell, and spit the Blood of his Redeemer from his mouth.

After that, the executioners knew they must be swift. The priests hurried away in horror. In their places, the other two advanced, hooded like the fates, converging from two directions.

For a while Basil fought them cleverly. If design had deserted him before, it came to him now, in the desperate and futile instinct of an animal that has been surrounded and defeated. He knew the swing of the giant blade would have to catch him neatly on the neck. So he decided to make his neck as small as possible. He did not try to elude those two messengers of doomsday. Instead, he waited for them, his shoulders hunched up, his neck buried between them. In the center of the scaffold, he crouched like an owl, like a bird of darkness immune from evil, two steely eyes blinking in the face of danger.

But these men were tempered in their calling. They had hunted many men before him, and they were familiar with such desperate wiles. That was why there were two of them. One raised the huge, curved blade; and as Basil had predicted, he could not find the two or three inches of flesh to make the clean cut. The blade was still poised in the air, hovering. In the meantime, the other executioner did his work. (They worked together, those two celebrants of death.) With the pointed sword he gave Basil a poke in the ribs, drawing blood, then fell flat against the floor. Involuntarily, Basil shuddered with the pain. His back arched, his head popped up from between his shoulders, and his neck elongated. That instant, the second dancer did his pirouette, with the long, curved glistening blade. From where he lay, safely against the platform, one executioner saw it against the sky—one enormous, glittering arc. Then, the next instant, on the planking of the scaffold, fell Basil Kikos' head.

"And so the murderer was punished," said Old Yia-Yia.

"And so the Virago's vendetta was concluded," said Uncle George.

"And so the *vrykolakas* was quelled before he rose," say I.

"But where is the *vrykolakas?*" said Uncle Manuel (another

voice added to the chorus) once when we discussed the story. "And why do you call the story a vendetta? There were no vendettas in Kasos. The Kasiots were a peaceful people, not like the Cretans and Maniots. The widow wanted Basil Kikos to be executed because he was lawfully convicted of her husband's murder, and his life would pay for her husband's life."

But wasn't that a vendetta too, since Basil Kikos was not guilty and even the judges wanted him to go free? Even if the Kasiots did not fight blood feuds like the Cretans and the Maniots, they had at least this one vendetta. For the same reason, the *vrykolakas,* too, is self-evident. Though a *vrykolakas* need never have actually risen from the grave, he was a lurking image of the deceased, calling forth conflicting emotions in the mourner's soul until he seemed actually to embody them, to personify them in visible form. A *vrykolakas* could be a haunting in the soul quieted somehow by the time all the memorials had been sung. And a *vrykolakas,* in a darker and more violent form, would have danced in the imagination of the Virago, as she kissed the broad, curved instrument of execution.

"Come quickly, Elias," called Uncle George, one evening in Kasos. "I found the Virago."

I hurried to his room, expecting to find another effigy of evil, but instead I found a dignified portrait of some members of the Malliarakis family: several tall men in high collars and well-clipped beards, and sitting among them, as kindly a Kasiot mother as I have seen. She was a small woman, in the black of mourning. Her face was peaceful, her eyes were soft; on her lap were a pair of folded, knobby hands.

"Not very fierce," I said, "for a virago."

"She wasn't fierce. Except for what happened on the square in Rhodes, she never committed any violence in her life."

Then it must have been a dream, coming on her as suddenly as any other dream (only in this case it lasted for a year), and left her when it passed from her, as cleansed of terror and compulsion as anyone on wakening. Actually, Old Yia-Yia was probably more of a virago than her mother, though she too never committed any violence in her life (except cutting up her husband's ledgers), and by the end of her life she had become so meek and helpless that she could say to her grandsons as pathetically as any orphan, "You mean, I don't have a mother anymore."

So a person you call the Virago might no more be one than a person you call Old Yia-Yia. This must be the way to exorcise viragos and *vrykolakas*, to discover them in the realm of the occult and trace their descent to the familiar. All along it was the mystery of the Virago which was the *vrykolakas*, just as the *vrykolakas* was the mystery of Virago. The *vrykolakas* was what was unresolved about her which made her remote and unfamiliar to the narrators of her story, so that she seemed bizarre and unnatural as a vampire herself, capable—as one of her great-grandsons believed—of drinking her victim's blood.

There is one more episode to be reported, and then we can lay the Virago to her rest. In 1911, Uncle George went to visit Old Yia-Yia in Alexandria. The Virago had been dead for many years, and little Marigo had now become a grandmother many times. Still hot-tempered and meddlesome, she had quarreled with relatives in Syros and departed in a fury for Alexandria on the pretext of visiting her sons (no doubt muttering "You hear? You hear?"). When Uncle George came to her house, he was told that Old Yia-Yia was not at home. She had gone to Port Said to sing dirges by the bier of a Kasiot gentleman recently deceased. Who was the Kasiot gentleman? A Mr. Kikos.

It was the same family. The new Mr. Kikos was a son of one of Basil's brothers, maybe the son of the murderer himself. The ceremony in Rhodes had been concluded, and now, sixty years later there was this new ceremony to take its place. There was an end of this latest Mr. Kikos, and little Marigo, who had denied mercy to the ancestor, hurried off to sing dirges for the descendant. Having attended one ceremony at the age of eight, Old Yia-Yia was at it again at sixty-eight.

"Oh, Mr. Kikos, black blood is flowing from my heart for you. Oh, Mr. Kikos, bitter was your communion."

Begging Your Pardon, Another Vengeance

I have always been confused by all the Turkish money in use in Kasos: piastres, paras, mezitia. Once during our stay, I asked Uncle George to explain it.

"Let's see," he said. "The Turkish pound was worth a hundred piastres. And the meziti was worth twenty piastres. There were smaller coins called kartakia and octarakia. And then there was an even smaller coin called . . . an even smaller coin called . . ."

His eyes were lifted to the ceiling.

"The metalik! I remember, the metalik."

"How many piastres to the metalik?"

"None. The metalik was smaller than a piastre. One piastre was worth four metaliks. Then there was another sub-division of the piastre called a para."

"What was a para?"

"A fortieth of a piastre. Every piastre was worth forty paras, but the metalik was independent of the para, and its value varied from place to place. When I said the piastre was worth four metaliks, I meant only in Constantinople. In Salonika, for example, the piastre might be worth 3.5 metaliks, in Beirut perhaps 3.25, in Smyrna 3."

"Good God."

"So now do you understand Turkish money?"

"I understand why the Ottoman Empire collapsed."

"Now, by the way, I'll tell you something else the Virago did in Rhodes, and to understand the story, all you have to remember is that there were forty paras to the piastre."

"Forty paras to the piastre."

"That's right. Now the Virago had taken all her children to the cafe, with a maid who was accompanying them, an earlier version of Aphrodite named Artemia. Suddenly, the Virago had a craving for eggplants, and so she told Artemia to get some from the green grocer. In Rhodes, the Virago knew, the egg-plants grew to be very long—very long indeed—one foot long . . ."

"I beg your pardon."

"The eggplants grew to be very long, as they still do, one foot long . . . Oh yes, of course, excuse me! The eggplants— begging your pardon—grew to be very long. By your indul-gence, they were one foot long. And very tender."

And so, with apologies, Uncle George told of the Virago's craving for eggplants, and the satisfaction of that craving in— begging your pardon—another vengeance.

"How many shall I get?" said Artemia.

"Oh, one piastre's worth," said the Virago, and she gave Artemia a piastre. Now the Virago was reckoning on the price in Kasos. Even today, Kasos produces no vegetables at all, and very little fruit, only a few grapes and figs. Vegetables have to be imported from Rhodes or Karpathos, and the price in-cludes the transportation. But in Rhodes the land is very fertile, and fruit and vegetables are abundant, and the eggplants— begging your pardon—are very long and tender. So Artemia went off to the green grocer with her piastre for the eggplants.

"How many do you want?" said the green grocer.

"One piastre's worth," said Artemia.

"One piastre's worth?"

"That's right."

"In that case," said the green grocer, "open your arms."

Artemia opened her arms, and the green grocer laid the eggplants across, very long eggplants, very long and tender. How many eggplants in Artemia's arms? Forty! In Rhodes, eggplants cost one para each, and there were forty paras in the piastre. Forty eggplants in Artemia's arms! She came back to the cafe carrying the eggplants like firewood, hardly able to see over the top of them. And when the Virago saw her coming, she said, "What evil is this?" and Artemia said, "Didn't you tell me to buy one piastre's worth of eggplants. Here they are, one piastre's worth, forty eggplants."

And with that, the Virago picked up one of the forty eggplants—a very ripe and tender one—and struck Artemia on the head.

Let Him Cast the First Stone

I would be a poor grandson of Kasos if I did not tell something of its shipping history. The land was always poor, without water or topsoil, and since a living could not be wrested from it, the islanders turned naturally to the sea. Savary found the island inhabited mostly by women and old men. The able men were sailing on the Archipelago, carrying their share of the Mediterranean and Black Sea trade. As early as the Revolution, there was a shipbuilding yard at the ancient harbor of Imborio, where the Kasiots constructed their ships out of lumber cut from Asia Minor. Kasos was a *thalassocracy,* a society dominated by the sea. Status was acquired in it according to the place a man had won in the shipping life of the island. However lowly a man's task might be, it was respectable so long as it was related to the sea and shipping. A shipwright was an honorable trade, a house-carpenter was not. Those trades related only to the land—tilling fields or building houses—were too lowly to be performed by anyone but migrant Karpathians.

In 1821, Kasos put to sea fifteen ships over a hundred tons, mostly brigs and schooners. There were about twenty shipping families at that time, each ruled by one man who acted as the captain of the ship; his younger brothers, cousins, nephews, and the relations of his wife all sailed under his command. That practice has endured to this day, when the owners of the ships no longer sail with them, and that is why although Greek shipping has become a multi-million dollar industry, it is owned and operated mostly in family groups.

During the Egyptian invasion, all the Kasiot ships were either destroyed or towed away, and in the years after the Revolution, the Kasiots had to rebuild their merchant navy from the beginning. When Ludwig Ross arrived in 1847, he saw new ships on the ways at Imborio, the ships of a new Kasiot generation. They were men whose names did not appear on the list of captains in 1821—Elias of the Fez, Hazimanolis Malliarakis, the Kikos family, and others—building ships in the tradition they had learned from their forbears. But because of the loss they had suffered in 1824, the Kasiots had fallen far behind the wealthier merchants of Hydra and Spetsai, and to regain their position in the Archipelago, they had to sail continually against the wind. Already, by the middle of the century, shipping was beginning the difficult transition from sail to steam, a period which inflicted hardship on everyone and eventually destroyed whoever could not adjust to it.

At that time, many Kasiots sought a surer livelihood. Ferdinand de Lesseps had won support for a project eventually to become the Suez Canal, and seamen from all over the world began to migrate to the isthmus to seek employment. A large number of Kasiots were among the first to arrive, and since their seamanship was well known, de Lesseps favored them from the beginning. In the early years they lived under primitive and unsanitary conditions, assisting in the cutting of the canal. Then, after the city of Port Said was founded, they moved into the

large section of it which has remained a Kasiot quarter to this
day. In 1867, when the Canal was opened, the first pilot to pass
through it was a Kasiot. (Later, when the Panama Canal was
opened, its first pilot was once again a Kasiot.)

The Kasiots became pilots and captains of dredgers, earning
salaries many times what they could have earned on sailing
ships. They became the first Greek community in modern
Egypt, eventually reaching a population of 6,000, enjoying all
the benefits of French colonialists. Besides their high salaries,
they were granted ample pensions and frequent summer vaca-
tions. Through co-operative societies set up by the Canal Company, they learned French, acquired the French habits and
customs, and bought French goods at reduced rates and pre-
ferential duties. By 1890, they had become the aristocracy of
Kasos, returning to the island during summer months to stroll
on their native rock in white suits and shoes and hats from Paris.
Uncle George, as a Kasiot boy dressed in the lowly smock of
the island children, remembers envying playmates returned
from Egypt in their brilliant white.

But the story of the sea is full of flux, and though one wave
has risen to certain height, there may be another to follow which
will rise even higher. Although these vacationeers from Suez
were the envy of the island in 1890, there were other Kasiots
about to make fortunes on the sea which would make the salaries and pensions of the Suez Canal Company seem insignif-
icant. At the beginning of the century and during the First
World War, shipping rates were to reach such a level that if a
man had even one share in a single ship, he could multiply his
wealth many times. The Kasiots who would reap that sudden
harvest were not those who had traded an uncertain life at sea
for the security of a fixed salary and pension, but those whom
the emigration to Egypt had left behind, the islanders who had
remained with their ships and managed the hazardous transition
to the age of steam.

These men were Captain Elias and his contemporaries, who from 1898 to 1910, sold their sailing ships to buy steamships. (Captain Elias sold the *Anastasia* in 1898, used the proceeds to buy shares in a steamship, the first one to be owned even partially by a Kasiot.) These men were yet another generation of seafarers, and very few of them appear among those who reconstructed the Kasiot fleet after the Revolution. These were the Kasiots who took the greatest risks, and who, in proportion to what they started with, reaped the greatest returns. Their descendants control the merchant fleet of Kasos today. Like my own family, after migrating to Syros at the end of the century, they moved on to London after the First World War. Then, in 1939, some of them extended the journey to America.

In the meantime, Greek shipping has changed since the days when the ships of the Greek islands fought the Turkish fleet. The fleets of Hydra, Spetsai, and Psara have vanished from the sea, and ships of other islands are sailing in their places—Chios, Syros, Ithaca, Cephalonia—as well as ships owned by Greeks not from any island in particular. Of the islands that put ships to sea in 1821, only Kasos does today. While Kasiots sailed on brigs and schooners during the Revolution, now they sail on freighters and tankers. While in 1821 the fleet of Kasos totaled fifteen hundred tons, now it totals nearly two million. Though the present Kasiot owners operate their ships from London and New York, they are still faithful to their ancestral island. Though some of them have never set foot on Kasos, they continue to employ Kasiot captains and seamen on their ships, often the descendents of men their forbears had employed before them.

Every able Kasiot seaman is employed on a ship owned by a son or grandson of the island, not only those remaining on the island but many times that number who have departed into *xenitia*. Their paychecks are sent home regularly to the island, and their houses are kept in excellent condition, standing out among the rubble in brilliant colors and a blinding gypsum white.

In this way, the destiny of the island is still with the sea. A traveler to Kasos today would find, like Savary, an island inhabited by women and old men. Though the face of the waters is ever-changing, the island is still living by its ships.

Now, in a brilliant history, there are two dark matters which must be mentioned. The first is that at the time of the Revolution, Kasiot captains engaged in piracy. From 1821 to 1824, one of the principle activities of the Kasiot fleet was to intercept neutral ships bearing cargoes to the Turks. When the Kasiots blockaded Crete, the neutral governments claimed that since Greece was not a nation and could not legally impose a blockade, these activities of the Kasiots were acts of piracy. A prodigious scholar of Kasiot history, Dr. Nicholas Mavris, edited *The Archive of Kasos*, a collection of all documents referring to the role of Kasos in the Revolution. It contains evidence of constant complaints of the French, British, and Austrian authorities against the Kasiot harassments of neutral ships and attempts to get reparations out of the *Demogerontia* of Kasos. According to another historian, when the Egyptians finally sacked the island, they found the Kasiot storehouses full of goods obviously stolen from Turkish, Egyptian, or neutral ships. Yet another claims that after 1824 when such activities of the Kasiot fleet were at an end, the insurance companies of Trieste and Marseilles actually lowered their rates.

Dr. Mavris has written a pamphlet called "Were the Kasiots Pirates?" in which he attempts to draw a distinction between pirates and corsairs. Pirates, he says, stole for personal gain, while corsairs stole for a political purpose. Since Kasiots intercepted only those ships bearing cargoes to the enemy, Dr. Mavris concluded, the Kasiots were corsairs.

But if the Kasiots were corsairs, I believe they also could

have been pirates. If they could have stolen for a political purpose, they also could have stolen for personal gain. Dr. Mavris' own archives contain evidence of Kasiot raids on the neighboring islands of Rhodes and Kos in which they stole provisions not from Turks or Austrians or Englishmen, but from fellow Greeks. Considering the low opinion the Kasiots had of their landlubbering neighbors the Karpathians, it is safe to assume they stole from them. And we cannot read of the Kasiot exploits during the Revolution—the raid on the Sultan's ships at Damietta as well as countless other damages—without suspecting what they could do before 1821, when such acts could not be interpreted strictly as evidence of piety and patriotism.

As to the maritime activity of the Kasiots before the Revolution, we know nothing more than what the womenfolk of Kasos told Savary, which understandably was not very much. There is an epic poem survived on Kasos to this day, describing an incident supposed to have taken place in 1819, two years before the Revolution. Three Kasiot captains, sailing southward out of the Dardanelles, met three Arab pirates, overtook them, and carried them off to Kasos with their crews and booty. The moral of the poem is contained in a prose postscript. "In the year 1830," reads the written version which survives, "the French fleet delivered mankind from *Algerian* piracy." (My italics.) Thus, the intention of the poem is all too clear. It celebrates certain proficiencies of the Kasiots, which in themselves are the proficiencies of pirates—overtaking ships, subduing crews, taking booty—while at the same time it cleverly puts the Kasiots on the side of law and order, and leaves the stigma of piracy where it belongs, with Algerian heathens.

Like any elaboration on historical fact, this legend is made of true material. The Algerian and other Arab pirates were a far greater scourge on the Aegean than the Kasiots. And the only falsehood in the story is not stated but implied: that the Kasiots were the enemies not only of other pirates, but of piracy as well.

Here, the familiar Kasiot saying has another application: "With whatever teacher you sit down with, that's the lesson you will learn." The early Kasiots sat down with Turkish, Venetian, Algerian, and other Arab teachers, and it is inconceivable that they could not only have survived but flourished under such austere schooling without learning certain lessons all too well. Since Kasos itself was within easy striking distance of the trade routes between Constantinople and the outlying provinces of the Ottoman Empire—Crete, Rhodes, Cyprus, Syria, and Egypt—the Kasiots must have had ample opportunity to practice what they learned.

After the Revolution, there was one final eruption of piracy in the Aegean. The French and British fleets worked hard to clean out the islands, and by 1830, piracy was at an end. Now, as Greece took its first steps as a modern nation and began to develop its great potential for a shipping industry, a second fact emerges in the history of Kasos.

Even after the end of piracy, there was both an honest and a dishonest way to make a living, for Kasiots as well as other seamen. During the difficult days of the late nineteenth century, an honest captain had to ply the sea continually, accepting any unprofitable cargo for any faraway port (like Captain Elias' roof-tiles which kept him tied up in Syros for a whole winter). Unless he had a cargo for Alexandria and could stop on the way, often he would not return to his native island for eighteen months or a full two years. (I used to wonder why so many Kasiot children were born exactly two years apart; I naïvely asked what contraceptual devices were available to their parents. None, of course: the husbands were at home in Kasos only once in two years.) In this way, a Kasiot captain spent most of his life on the sea, working hard, to be rewarded only at the end of the century, if he could endure long enough to share in the coming boom. Naturally, there were some Kasiot captains who disliked hard work, some who preferred to spend their winters on their native island, roistering in the cafés. These Kasiots found another way, the second nefarious maritime practice, known as barratry.

It was customary at that time, as it is today, for the cargo owner to charter a captain's ship at a given rate. After the agreement had been reached, the captain would simply load the cargo on his ship and sail away with it; and unless the charterer posted a representative or supercargo to accompany the ship and protect his interests, he would have to trust the captain for the duration of the voyage. The voyages of sailing ships lasted several weeks, and during that time, anything might happen. The captain might encounter heavy weather and find himself in danger of foundering unless he lightened his ship by jettisoning all his extra masts and rigging and even a portion of the cargo if necessary. In that event, under the laws of general average, the captain would not be responsible for the loss of cargo, and it would have to be sustained solely by the charterer. This was where certain captains were cunning enough to see a special opportunity. A captain might not encounter heavy weather at all, only *claim* to have encountered it.

The coasts of the Aegean Islands and mainland Greece are full of tiny coves, secret places where a ship might put in unnoticed, under the cover of a moonless night. There, by prearrangement, a caique might come out to meet the ship, and as it drew alongside, the captain might strike a stealthy bargain with the caique's owner to *sell* him a portion of the cargo. After the agreement had been concluded, a portion of the cargo would be lowered into the caique. The captain would sail out onto the high seas again, then to the island of Zante where there were certain legal experts. They could doctor the log of the voyage to show that on such and such a day, under the stress of heavy weather, the captain had found it necessary to jettison his extra masts and spars and sails (items which might never have existed) as well as that portion of the cargo he had actually sold. At the conclusion of the voyage, the captain would enjoy a double profit: the rate of hire agreed upon with the charterer, plus the proceeds of the sale. Then, his winter's work done in a single voyage, he could return to his native island and roister in the café.

The practice was widespread in the Aegean after the Revolution, taking the place of piracy of old. The island of Zante, which had probably begun as a natural haven for mariners after a storm, became a nest of log doctorers. Gradually, it became so common for captains to put into Zante after the sale of cargo, that underwriters refused to pay a claim if the ship had stopped there for any reason. Meanwhile, the Greek Government, anxious to protect the reputation of its growing merchant marine, ran down offenders and imposed heavy penalties on them. And wherever Greek captains were suspected of barratry, the Greek Government posted a consul to report any illegal sales.

Barratry became very popular among certain Kasiots. It appealed to their naturally wily nature, as much for its own sake as for any profit it would yield. They would sail home to Kasos, anchor outside the Bucca and sell a portion of the cargo to the island merchants. Then, sending the ship on to Zante to its doctors, they would ascend victorious to the cafe.

But no Kasiot ever got rich on barratry, and the names of the barrators have dropped long ago from the shipping history of the island. After the captain had sold the cargo, he would be open to blackmail at the hands of his very accomplices; and often in the years ahead, he would have to pay out much more than he had made by the original transaction.

Sometime in the latter half of the nineteenth century, a Kasiot captain whom we can call Captain Nikos put into Salonika to find a cargo. It was a very slack season, and cargoes were difficult to find, so for lack of anything better he contracted with two Jewish rabbis to carry a cargo of flagstones at a very unprofitable rate. But the rabbis rubbed salt into his wounds.

"You're a Kasiot, aren't you?" they said.

Captain Nikos said he was.

"Well, in that case we shall have to post supercargoes to keep watch over our flagstones."

"Very well," said Captain Nikos, taking no offense at this discrimination. "Who will be your supercargoes?"

"We will," said the rabbis. "Both of us."

"You will?" said Captain Nikos, smiling. "Very well."

So the rabbis packed their belongings and prepared to sail with Captain Nikos to keep watch over their flagstones. And in the meantime, Captain Nikos was thinking: "Two supercargoes to watch over flagstones? What they must think of me? If I sold all their stones at twice their value, I still would not make enough to pay for my expenses. But very well. Let them come if they wish. I will see they have an exciting voyage."

In the meantime, an idea had grown on him. The rabbis had heard so much about the mischief of certain Kasiots, Captain Nikos thought he could not very well disappoint them. Since they distrusted him so openly, even with a cargo of flagstones, he would not be one to let them down. He would sell their cargo anyway, worthless as it was, under their very noses.

So Captain Nikos set sail from Salonika, already smirking over what he planned; and the two rabbis sailed with him. Standing stiffly on either side of the tiller in their black robes and beards and broad brimmed black hats, they watched Captain Nikos with eagle eyes. When the ship sailed out beyond the harbor, a strong wind came up. And although the rabbis did not realize it, Captain Nikos did what any seaman knows not to do. He steered the ship broadside to the wind, so that immediately it began to roll.

"What's that?" said the rabbis, taken by surprise.

"The wind," said Captain Nikos.

"Ah, the wind," said the rabbis solemnly, composing themselves once again on either side of Captain Nikos. But now the ship was rolling so fiercely they had trouble keeping their balance. Though neither of them said a word and did not even look at each other, very soon they were both pale as ghosts.

"Is this normal?" said one rabbi at last, in a voice weak with nausea and with fear.

"As normal as the wind," said Captain Nikos.

"But what will happen?"

"I don't know. If you wish, you may go below where you can lie down and be more comfortable."

The rabbis looked at each other. For one longing moment they looked in the direction of their cabin. But at last, bravely, they decided against it.

"No, we must stay here to keep watch over our flagstones," they said.

"Very well," said Captain Nikos, raising his voice above the wind and water. "But if you must stand here, at least take hold of something. I'm afraid you may be thrown into the sea."

At that moment, appearing to be steering carefully in the face of danger, Captain Nikos turned the wheel violently one way and then the other, so that the ship plunged down toward the menacing white water, reprieving itself from catastrophe at the last moment, only to plunge down toward it again on the other side.

"But what is happening?" cried the rabbis. "Is this a storm?"

"Yes," said Captain Nikos, "a storm."

"Is it a bad one? Is it dangerous?"

"Any storm is a bad one, but this is the most dangerous storm I ever seen."

"God of Moses. But what will happen? Will we drown?"

"We may," said Captain Nikos. "We are so heavy and the wind is so strong that at any moment we may go over."

"Go over? You mean into the sea?"

"Into the sea."

"God of Aaron, and is there nothing we can do?"

"Do? What should we do?"

"Is there nothing we can do to save ourselves?"

"Of course."

"What?"

"Pray. Pray to your God."

"*Pray to our God?* Is there nothing else?"

"Is that not enough?"

"God of Moses, is there nothing we can do to save *ourselves?* If we are so heavy, can't we lighten?"

"Lighten? How lighten?"

"If a ship is too heavy, they say the captain can throw some of the cargo overboard."

"Throw some of the cargo overboard?" said Captain Nikos. "*You* are asking *me* to throw some of the cargo overboard?"

"Why not?" cried the rabbis. "That would save us, wouldn't it? We would be lighter then, and we would be able to make it through this storm."

"Of course we would. We would be lighter in an instant, and the ship would right itself and be out of danger, and then there would be an end to this terrible sickness and dizziness and rolling first one way and then the other."

"Oh, dear God of Isaac, then let us lighten! God of Jacob, let us throw some of the cargo overboard."

"No," said Captain Nikos. "Upon my honor, as a captain and as a Kasiot, no."

"But why? Why in the name of God?"

"Because later, when we reached our destination, you would say we did not meet bad weather at all, that I didn't really throw the cargo overboard but sold it for my own profit. And as a Kasiot captain, I would rather drown than hear such accusations."

"Say you sold the cargo? Captain Nikos, put it out of your mind! We trust you completely!"

"Then why did you sail with me to watch over your cargo? That is the reason you find yourselves in this needless danger when you could be safe in your homes this very moment."

By now, the rabbis were close to tears.

"Oh, why, Captain Nikos? We do not know why! We wish we had never sailed with you. But that is all forgotten. We promise you, on the bones of all the prophets, we shall never sail with you again. Only please, Captain Nikos, throw some of our flagstones overboard. You can trust us, Captain Nikos. We will sign a paper. We will do anything you say. Only please, Captain Nikos, before it is too late."

Captain Nikos deliberated for one unendurable moment.

"Very well," he said, "if you insist, I agree. But one of you must begin. That one." He pointed to one rabbi. "Let it be him. Let him cast the first stone."

"I will, I will," said the rabbi. "Only hurry, for the love of God, hurry before all is lost."

Captain Nikos directed his crew to open the cargo hatch and lift out one of the stones for the rabbi to throw overboard. As agreed, the rabbi awkwardly cast the first stone. Afterwards, at a signal from Captain Nikos, the seamen began to lift out a few of the stones, one by one, and throw them overboard. At that moment, Captain Nikos manipulated the wheel in such a way that a huge wave curled over the side and almost broke upon the rabbis.

"For the love of God," cried Captain Nikos, "go below now, or the next wave will carry you away."

Without a word, the rabbis scurried below out of the menacing sea and wind. As soon as they disappeared, Captain Nikos ordered his men to stop what they were doing.

"What are you doing there, my lads?" he said. "Throwing stones into the sea? Have you lost your minds?"

Laughing, the crew stopped throwing stones into the sea, closed the hatch, and went about their business. After a discreet interval, Captain Nikos steered out of the wind, as any landlubber knows he should. The ship righted itself, and the storm subsided into a placid Aegean afternoon.

The rabbis, by that time, were sound asleep. Delivered from

the jaws of death and the terrible nausea which had menaced them far worse, they slept through the dinner hour and far into the night. And they were still asleep, near midnight, when Captain Nikos sailed into a deserted cove, and beckoning the owner of a caique to draw alongside, sold him the remaining flagstones. The next day, sailing toward their destination on an empty ship, the rabbis signed a paper Captain Nikos had prepared, attesting to the fact that the ship had met heavy weather a few miles out of Salonika, and at their insistence, the captain agreed to jettison the cargo. One of the rabbis, they admitted, had cast the first stone.

Captain Nikos' story became proverbial on Kasos. He was such a notorious barrator, he would sell flagstones for the sport of it, and he became the first Kasiot in history to get his supercargoes to doctor the log.

These are the facts in the shipping history of Kasos. Some we can repeat with pride, others we must remember with a smile. But if there is anyone who wants to dwell on some facts more than others, any member of another fleet—some grandson of Hawkins, Drake or Erikson, then we can say to him, as Captain Nikos said to the rabbis, "Let him cast the first stone."

The
Hollow
Crown

*S*ometime before the end of the last century, an eligible Kasiot bachelor named Dr. Nikolakis tried to solve the riddle of how a man should marry. In Kasos, marriages were usually arranged by the families of the bride and groom in a process known as *proxenia*. In this process, the initiative must always come from the woman's family. A man could not simply ask a girl to marry him, or people would think he was so ineligible he could not get a wife any other way. Instead, he would drop a hint to the girl's family, indicating that he would welcome a proposal if it were offered. At a feast on the square before the church, as he looked the girl's father carefully in the eye, he might sing a *mandinadha*, composed especially for the occasion:

> "A flower blooms in your courtyard,
> Fairer than all others on the island."

Everyone would pass off the *mandinadha* without a second thought, as a forced and empty rhyme. But to the girl's father, the rhyme would not be empty at all. If he found this bridegroom to his liking, on the next moonless evening, he would set out with his male relations to make the *proxenia.* Putting on socks of different colors for good luck, and holding a lantern before them to light their way, they would pay a visit to this would-be bridegroom. If he accepted the *proxenia,* the party would come home singing *mandinadhas,* and by morning everyone would know of the impending marriage. But if for some reason he did not accept it, or if his answer were equivocal in the least, the delegates would come home as silently as they had gone out, with even the lantern burning furtively.

After the *proxenia,* the next question was the dowry, which no judicious bridegroom should neglect. There was nothing covert or surreptitious about it. When the delegates offered the girl's hand in marriage, they disclosed the total of the dowry, to help the man make up his mind. If he accepted, the next ceremony would be the *emvasmata* or formal betrothal when for the first time the bridegroom would step across the girl's threshold as her bridegroom-to-be. Just before this ceremony, before the man had taken this irrevocable step, the girl's father would sign a document called the *prikosimfonon* in which he would list the items of his daughter's dowry, her house and lands and the sum of cash he had provided for her. The combined families and bride and groom would witness the conclusion of this agreement; a notary public would affix his seal, and the *demogeronts* of the island would attest it. From then on, the *prikosimfonon* was filed away in the archives of the island, binding the father-in-law to his agreement. But in practice, the bridegroom was well advised to have the coins of his dowry safely in his pocket before his wedding. Otherwise, once he married the girl, all his bargaining position would be lost, and it was very likely that the father-in-law, having reaped all advantage from the promise would never be made to pay the price. In such cases, popular sympathy was all with the wily father-in-law, and there is even a Kasiot saying on the subject:

> For coins printed on a paper,
> Don't lose a bridegroom in the flesh.

The *prikosimfonon* was actually a title of inheritance, a title to ancestral property as distinct from property acquired in the parent's lifetime. In her *prikosimfonon,* a first daughter received the house and lands which had been her mother's before her as well as other ancestral property and a sum of cash provided by her father as a dowry. A first son also had a *prikosimfonon,* including ancestral property falling to his name. If the first-born did not marry, he did not receive his ancestral property; and at the end of his life, it would be awarded by a council of the family to another heir who bore the same first name. Similarly, if the first-born died without issue, the ancestral property must also be returned. If a woman died without issue, which often happened as a result of complications in the first pregnancy, her husband could not retain her ancestral property and dowry but must return it to her family who would then reassign it as before.

After the heir received his inheritance in his *prikosimfonon,* there was always the danger that he would be less dutiful to his parents than before. For this reason, Kasiot custom allowed the parent to withhold a portion of the heir's ancestral property, called a *yerontomoiri.* After the parent's death, the *yerontomoiri* would be returned to the heir, providing he had been dutiful and cared for his parents throughout their later life. Otherwise, the parents had the right to will the *yerontomoiri* to anyone who had cared for them instead.

The marriage customs anticipated everything, except the feelings of the bride and groom. In the poetry and songs of Kasos, young men might promise to come for their beloveds in ships with silken sails; but in reality, Kasiot weddings came about without such promises, except those promises listed in the *prikosimfonon*. A young man might sing of love in *mandinadhas*, but when it came time for him to choose a wife, he did not come for her in any ship of silken sail, but invited her father and her uncles to come to him.

There was always another way to marry, outside the custom, according to the heart. But in a custom-bound society such as Kasos, this way was equivalent to revolution. Dr. Nikolakis chose this way. To his own surprise, Dr. Nikolakis became a revolutionary and embraced the cause of liberty. In this matter more fraught with custom and coercion than any other, he alone found the courage to confront his oppressor and declare, "To such a tyrant, I will not kneel."

He started looking for a wife almost as soon as he returned from medical school in Athens to begin his career as the island doctor. He was thirty years old, the eldest in his family. He had a brother, Yani, who was twenty-eight, and a sister, Eloula, who was twenty. His father had been lost at sea when all the children were very young. His mother was a strong-willed Kasiot woman who had worn black most of her life and brought up her children alone. She had doted on her first son, Dimitri, who had always been first in his class and went to study medicine in Athens and returned as the island doctor. And she doted on her first daughter, Eloula, who must have a good dowry so that she could marry in accordance with the standing of her family. But between this prince and princess, Yani, the second son, was practically forgotten. Though Mother Nikolakis ruled Dimitri and Eloula with an iron hand, Yani had almost perfect freedom.

After school he used to spend his afternoons in the fields and vineyards, stealing fruit from under the eyes of the official watchmen hiding in the trees. And it was not long before he roamed the fields in the evening too, with Karpathian working girls, far from home and parents, willing to spend the night on the floors of unfinished houses, kicking at the moon.

When he finished grade school, Yani went to sea, and his mother hardly realized that he was gone. No one in Kasos heard of him for many years, until the winter when this tale began, when a Kasiot sailing ship anchored in the lee of Makra Island and many young men came ashore who would be bridegrooms before the spring. One of them—though no one would have suspected it—was Yani Nikolakis.

"Eh, Yani, when are you getting married?" someone in the cafe would say, and then there would be great laughter and all the old men would rock on their stools. For the joke was that Yani Nikolakis was not an eligible bridegroom. This habitué of the Bucca and regular companion of notorious Karpathian girls was not the sort of man likely to receive a delegation on a moonless night.

But the joke was on the old men of the Bucca after all, and on the Kasiot marriage system. For at that moment, Yani actually intended to get married. His wedding bed was all prepared —in an abandoned sheepfold in the hills—and he had already chosen the girl to take to it: Calliope, the fourth daughter of Captain Petros, a not-too-wealthy gentleman from Panayia.

Yani had seen her with her family at a feast in Panayia. He thought her beautiful, though others might say she was too short. And though some said she was feeble-minded, giggling foolishly the way she did, Yani thought her cheerful and good-natured. In short, he loved her, and he was blind to all her faults, including the outstanding one that as a fourth daughter she obviously would have no dowry.

One day Yani saw Calliope buying fruit in Phry.

"Sleep in your *moussandra* tonight," he said, standing next to her, turning a melon in each hand. "Sleep in your *moussandra* and leave the window open."

In Captain Petros' house, the *moussandra* opened onto a balcony that extended out beyond the courtyard wall. It was high enough so that people walking in the street below could not reach it, but if a man came by on muleback, taking hold of the railing, he could swing himself onto the balcony. In addition, if the window had been left open, he could then get into the *moussandra*.

Calliope did as she was told, for a reason not hard to understand; for if a fourth daughter of a not-too-wealthy captain is so timorous she lets such a chance go by, she deserves the life of spinsterhood bound to follow.

That night, Yani waited until all the lights were blown out in the houses of the island; the only sounds were stray dogs howling on the hillsides and the unending sea washing against the iron shore. His house was in Ayia Marina, high on a mountain above the sea. After midnight, he rode his mule out of Ayia Marina, downhill past the cemetery, between the dry-stone walls on either side, through the narrow labyrinthine streets of Phry, and uphill toward Panayia on the other side.

In the meantime, in the *moussandra*, Calliope was lying in the dark, her black eyes shining like an owl's above her blankets. Suddenly, out of the silence of the night, the shutters parted and a man's figure appeared on the balcony, framed against the sky.

"Come," he whispered to Calliope.

And she came. Yani wrapped the blanket around her, then jumped onto the mule ahead of her. Following him, completely trusting, Calliope fell into his arms.

Yani's heart was beating wildly as they rode away, two of them in one saddle, the mule's footsteps falling in the streets of Panayia as gently as summer hail. Outside Panayia, Yani turned the mule across the plain toward Arvanitohori. He had no more thought for silence now, shouting to the mule, and lashing its haunches with his stick. And now Calliope was beyond the power of any mortal to recall her. Now they were alone on that deserted plain, barren and sharply rutted with volcanic rock. They made their way across it into the more tender bed of a rain torrent, riding uphill toward Arvanitohori. Then, just below the town, Yani slipped down and led the mule across the rocky bed, Calliope holding fast to the saddle, still wrapped in her blanket: a virgin fleeing to the promised land.

When they had crossed the torrent, Yani mounted again, prodding the mule up to a road high on the shoulders of the mountain, opposite the town of Arvanitohori across a huge canyon opening like a lesion in the rock. There, they rode carefully, along the canyon's rim, past the chapel to St. Elias high on the mountain, until they found the sheepfold, sheltered beneath a cliff. There, in that homely bower, Yani concluded not only his *proxenia*, but his *emvasmata* and, for all practical purposes, his wedding too.

They had a simple ceremony, stripped of all custom but the essential one which any bridegroom knows and any bride can learn. Later in the week, Captain Petros would give his daughter to Yani Nikolakis (what could he do?) but that evening, without his assistance, in the hills near Arvanitohori, Calliope married him herself.

The next day, when the "wedding" was announced, it became the event of that bridal season. Captain Petros, wise enough to remember that this unexpected marriage had cost him nothing, took the news in stride. Kasiot custom had no authority over such revolutionary marriage, but it granted no advantage either. With neither formal *proxenia* nor *prikosimfonon* gone before, there could be no dowry. Once a man had stolen his bride, he could not pause to negotiate, for at that point he could not refuse to marry her without bringing the bullets of her kinsmen raining on his head.

Mother Nikolakis, for her part, cared just as much for this latest adventure of her second son as she had cared for his earlier ones.

"Let Yani do whatever he wants," she said. "My son the doctor will make the brilliant match."

In the meantime, to Dr. Nikolakis, lately returned from Athens, she sang golden prophecies.

"The girl you marry will be clever and obedient, respectful and intelligent," she said. "She must have not only a house and dowry, but fields and vineyards falling to her name in all the regions of the island. She must have mills and sheepfolds, chapels and holy icons and many gold Napoleons woven on her breast with golden thread. She must be the first daughter of a first daughter, descended in direct lineage from a noble Kasiot family, a true princess of the island."

"Who is she?" said Dr. Nikolakis. "Who is the noble daughter you have in mind?"

His mother was surprised.

"Why I don't know," she said. "I don't even know where to find her. You have the right to expect such perfection in a woman, that I'm afraid there is not one girl in Kasos worthy to become your bride."

Dr. Nikolakis was indeed an eligible man. He was tall and slender, with a well-trimmed black moustache and two curls separating gracefully in the middle of his forehead. His hair was always combed, and he always wore a frock coat and a high stiff collar with a firmly tied bow tie. Whenever they came to get him for a call, he would excuse himself to prepare his medicines, and in the privacy of his chamber, he would adjust his collar and comb his curls.

When he first arrived on Kasos, the island was stricken with an epidemic. Never had the Kasiot sun beat down more terribly, never had the "eye" worked greater evil. He was not on Kasos more than a few days when nearly every family in Ayia Marina suffered a case of sunstroke or some other ill. The epidemic spread, first to Phry and Arvanitohori, then to Poli and Panayia. Even the island's midwife and exorcist could find no charms against the blight. The only charm belonged to Dr. Nikolakis. Adjusting his tie and teasing his curls before every excursion, he had to visit every house, where, miraculously, on his arrival, the suffering patient would sit up in bed (invariably it was a young, unmarried girl) and her astonished mother would make a dozen crosses and swear that only an hour before the girl had trouble to open her eyes. Then, forgetting the miracle as instantly as it had occurred, this Kasiot mother would lead the doctor off into the *salla,* inquire politely after his mother, and ply him with cognac and candied fruit.

Then, one day, when Dr. Nikolakis had not been in Kasos very long, he received his first proposal. It happened in Panayia, in the house of his good friend, Captain Markos Phillipides. Captain Markos' daughter, Fifika, was known throughout the island as clever and obedient, respectful and intelligent. She had fields and vineyards, and many Napoleons woven on her breast with golden thread. She was a first daughter of a first daughter.

Dr. Nikolakis was fond of spending the afternoons with Captain Markos and his brother, and he used to visit them almost every day. One day, Captain Markos said, "Well, Dr. Nikolakis, your younger brother is already married, it won't be long before you take the crown." Then, the next day, he said, "Well, Dr. Nikolakis, your younger brother married a girl from Panayia. Surely our town can do as well for you."

Each time, teasing his curls and adjusting his tie, Dr. Nikolakis would lower his eyes and pretend he had not understood the hint. But he *had* understood, and he was thinking of the prospect more and more, and as he did so, he came more often than ever to the Phillipides' courtyard.

The Phillipides' took these visits as a counterhint, an indication that Dr. Nikolakis would accept a proposal if it were offered. Finally one afternoon, Captain Markos decided to bring the question out into the open.

It was a sunny day of the late winter. Dr. Nikolakis was sitting in the courtyard with the three Phillipides': Captain Markos, his younger brother Stavros, and his elder brother Petros, who was a little deaf. The town was quiet except for the occasional clatter of donkeys' footsteps in the streets. The sun began to set, the walls around the lots of Panayia turned redder and redder. Usually, these four friends would have been talking loudly, laughing, and slapping their knees. But this afternoon, for some reason, under the grapevine on the lattice overhead, the four friends crossed and uncrossed their legs in silence.

"By the way, Doctor," Captain Markos said at last, though from the sound of his voice, bravely beating back the silence, no one imagined this next topic could ever have arisen by the way. "By the way, Doctor, you know my daughter?"

Dr. Nikolakis looked at Captain Markos, as though he were being reminded of an unpaid debt.

"I mean Fifika, my first daughter," continued Captain Markos, in a low voice.

"Of course," muttered Dr. Nikolakis, "Fifika, your first daughter."

"No doubt you have seen her around the island," the captain said. "In church on Sundays and at the village feasts . . ."

"Ah yes," said Dr. Nikolakis. "In church on Sundays and at the village feasts."

"Yes, of course," said Captain Markos, mournfully. And as he looked at Dr. Nikolakis, Captain Markos realized that in another moment they would lapse into silence again.

"Well, you know she is really a very fine girl," he said.

"Indeed," said Dr. Nikolakis.

"Then you agree with me?"

"I certainly do."

"You mean you appreciate my daughter's virtues."

"Oh, yes, yes," said Dr. Nikolakis, "indeed I do."

"Splendid!" said Captain Markos, feeling better, moving his stool closer to the doctor's. "In that case, let me be a little indiscreet with you. Let me tell you something about my daughter's other assets. First of all there is her house, and everything inside it, crockery and silverware enough for a queen's table and linen enough for a queen's bed. And then there are fields and vineyards, mills and sheepfolds, chapels and holy icons. Now what do you say to that?"

Dr. Nikolakis stammered. "Wh-What should I say, Captain Markos?" he said. "If Fifika had nothing else, she would be inestimably lucky simply to be born your daughter."

"What's that? What's that?" said brother Petros, a hand cupped around his ear. "What's that the doctor says?"

"Nothing," said Captain Markos. "He says *she is a fine girl.*"

"A fine girl?" said brother Petros. "Why we *know* that. We've been sitting here for more than an hour, and all he can say is what we know already."

"All in good time," said Captain Markos, winking at the doctor. "Of course we know Fifika is a fine girl, but it makes us happy to hear the doctor thinks so too. And perhaps he thinks she is such a fine girl, he would like to know *even more* about her assets. Dr. Nikolakis, when you have seen my daughter at the village feasts, you may have noticed she has many sovereigns and Napoleons threaded on her breast."

"Indeed! Indeed!" said Dr. Nikolakis.

"So you have noticed."

"I have," said Dr. Nikolakis. Then, catching himself, he added, "but I do not value the gold which adorns the person so much as the person who adorns the gold."

"What a tongue this fellow has in his head!" said Captain Markos, slapping Dr. Nikolakis on the knee. "He has such command of Romaic, you hardly know what he's saying."

"What *is* he saying?" said deaf brother Petros.

"*He says he likes her,*" said brother Stavros.

"Then if he *likes* her, will he *marry* her?"

"That, no doubt," said Captain Markos, "is the very next thing we shall learn from him. We have all agreed that Fifika is a fine girl, and the doctor has just told us in his accustomed eloquence that, in plain language, he likes her. Now all we need to know from him is whether he will have her for his wife."

Dr. Nikolakis stammered again.

"O-only a madman would decline to have her," he said. "No man in his senses would decline to make his life among you with fair Fifika for his wife."

"What does he say?" said brother Petros, a hand upon his ear.

"He says *yes!*" said brother Stavros.

"Yes?" said brother Petros. "Well, I thought he'd keep us here all night."

"*Bravo*, Dr. Nikolakis," said Captain Markos.

"Welcome to our family," said brother Stavros.

"Glory to God," said brother Petros. "And now, if you'll excuse me, I'm going to bed. With all this talk I'm perfectly exhausted."

On the way home, Dr. Nikolakis realized to his surprise that his heart was beating wildly and his hands were trembling with excitement. Why should that be, he wondered? There was really nothing so remarkable in what had happened: the proposal had come at last, and at last he had accepted it. He had just become engaged to Fifika Phillipides and was going home to tell his mother.

At that point, his mother knew nothing of his marriage plans. Usually he told his mother everything he planned. But this time, for some reason, he had not. And now he didn't know why he was so excited. He didn't know why he was running, but he was running all the same. He ran up the road beyond the Bucca, past the contorted jungles of prickly pears, past carob and olive trees with shadows dancing in the road in gloomy ecstasy. Then he reached the town of Ayia Marina and ran through the narrow pebbled streets, among the houses huddled together like ascending or descending stairs. The bell was tolling at the church, the gates to courtyards swung ajar, and in the doorways stood hooded women—mothers, aunts, grandmothers—calling urchins from their play. In the rising wind of evening, the town seemed to be calling to its offspring with a woman's voice. And Dr. Nikolakis listened to the call and hurried to his mother.

She was in the courtyard when he arrived. At the sight of her, he wondered instantly how the proposal ever could have happened. At the sight of her, the last few hours seemed a dream, and he could not believe he had really become engaged to Fifika Phillipides or anyone else.

He opened the gate, as cautious and uneasy as any other child come home from mischief that afternoon. When his mother saw him, she kissed him on either cheek.

"Welcome to him!" cried Mother Nikolakis to her son. "Bring sugared almonds to welcome him and sacks of speckled pepper!"

Dr. Nikolakis wondered what was going on. Three hooded Nikolakis women were waiting with his mother.

"May the Virgin bless your arrival," said one.

"May your house be full of heirs," said the second.

"May your name never vanish from the island," said the third.

By that time, Dr. Nikolakis had some definite suspicions. Did the intention to marry show on a man's face with his telling? Were women so sensitive to this particular matter they could sense a wedding before it was announced?

"She's a fine girl," his mother said. "Clever and obedient, respectful and intelligent. She has fields and vineyards, chapels and holy icons, and many gold Napoleons woven on her breast. She is not all that you deserve, but as I have told you many times, there is no girl on Kasos who is. Still, to do her justice, no one has claimed she *does* deserve you. They have simply offered you her hand, and with a large dowry to go with it. So, in that case, I think she will do very nicely."

"I'm glad you like her," muttered Dr. Nikolakis, but secretly he was thinking: How could she know? Could the news of a man's *proxenia* travel faster than his feet?

"Glad I *like* her?" his mother was saying. "Of course I like her."

"Then you aren't angry I didn't tell you about it first?"

"Didn't tell me about it first? How could you? It just happened."

"That's what I was thinking. But how did you know? I've just come from there myself."

"Come from there yourself?" said Mother Nikolakis. "What do you mean? Come from where?"

"From the Phillipides'. I spent the whole afternoon with them."

"And what of that?" said Mother Nikolakis. "You are always wasting your time with them. Who is talking of the Phillipides'?"

"Who *are* you talking about?" said Dr. Nikolakis.

"The Yeroyioryis'."

"The Yeroyioryis'?"

"And their first daughter Marika."

"Their first daughter Marika?"

"Your *proxenia* was just concluded to her, to Marika Yeroyioryis."

"Marika Yeroyioryis?"

"Who did you think?"

"Fifika Phillipides."

"Fifika Phillipides? Whatever put such an idea in your head? Fifika Phillipides, indeed. Only an hour ago, Captain Manoli Yeroyioryis and his two brothers were right here where we are standing, making the proposal."

"And what did you say?"

"I said *yes.* They knew I would, since it was only my little hint that gave them nerve enough to make the proposal in the first place."

"And what did *they* say?"

"They were very happy. Oh, they did say, just as a formality, before the *proxenia* can be announced, they would like to talk to you themselves. They are coming back tomorrow morning, so do talk to them please, as a favor to me. It's just a formality. I can't blame them really. You are over thirty now, and I am only your poor mother, so I wouldn't dream of influencing you. So, tomorrow when they come, you can tell them it's all settled: then we can hold the *emvasmata* next Sunday, then the *prikos-imfonon* will be signed. And two Sundays from now, you will be married. Oh, dear boy, I can hardly believe this has happened."

"I can hardly believe it either," said Dr. Nikolakis.

For the time being, Dr. Nikolakis did what the most resolute bridegroom would have done: nothing. He said no more to his mother, only ate his dinner and went to bed. And that night, for many sleepless hours, Dr. Nikolakis pondered his first turning on the road to marriage.

If he had chosen revolution then, he would have solved his problem. He could have explained to the Yeroyioryis' what had happened, and though they would not have been pleased, they would have had to accept the fact. But the doctor was not yet a revolutionary. He was not accustomed to doing what he wanted, only what duty had prescribed for him.

He knew very well what the Yeroyioryis' would come to hear the next morning, and his problem was how to avoid saying it, without violating the precepts of the custom. The problem before him which he lay awake all night to solve, was how to avoid a proposal he could not accept, without actually refusing it, since that would have been just as impossible, owing to the fact that his mother had already accepted it on his behalf.

But incredibly enough, Dr. Nikolakis found a way.

"Only a madman would decline to have her," he said to the Yeroyioryis' the next morning. "No man in his senses would decline to make his life among you with fair Marika for his wife."

"Then it's settled," said Captain Manoli Yeroyioryis, getting up to kiss Dr. Nikolakis on both cheeks.

Dr. Nikolakis raised his arms to stop him. "If only it were settled," he said, "I would be the happiest man in Kasos."

"Then it isn't settled?" said the Captain.

"It isn't," said Dr. Nikolakis, "and for the time being, I'm afraid it cannot be. You see, gentlemen, I have a sister. Eloula is her name, and she has reached the age of twenty when she herself is ready to be married. As you know, gentlemen, according to the custom of the island, a man must marry off his sister before he can take a wife himself. If a girl's male relations do not help her find a husband, then how will she find a husband on her own? You know that, gentlemen, otherwise you yourselves would not be here with me this morning. A custom of our island brings your generous offer to me, and the very same custom prevents me from accepting it. As you are true to your Marika, I am true to my Eloula. You come to me to fulfill a gentle duty, and as that duty is fulfilled, so, at the same time, must it remain unfulfilled. Only by remaining unfulfilled can that gentle duty find fulfillment."

"What does he say?" said one of the Yeroyioryis brothers.

"I don't know," said Captain Manoli.

"Will he marry her?"

"Not for the time being."

"Why not?"

"Because he has a sister."

After the Yeroyioryis' had gone, Dr. Nikolakis collapsed into an armchair. But when his mother heard what had happened, she rushed in like a virago after vengeance.

"Are you in your senses?" she said. "What made you say such things?"

"My duty," said Dr. Nikolakis, without opening his eyes.

"Your duty! Squashes and cucumbers for your duty. Is this my reward, to be repaid with your disobedience and disrespect."

"On the contrary," said Dr. Nikolakis. "I am observing the custom of the island, and in doing so, I am most obedient and respectful."

"Squashes and cucumbers for the custom of the island. What help does Eloula need from you to find a husband? What help could you be to her, since you could not even find yourself a wife? When the time comes, I will find her a husband, just as I've found a wife for you. But she is too young to marry yet. For the time being, I want her with me."

"Then you shall have her," said Dr. Nikolakis, "and for the time being, you shall have me too."

"Christ and Virgin!" said Mother Nikolakis. "I don't know which of my sons is the greater curse, the one who never listens to a word I say, or the one who is so obedient."

But for the time being, Dr. Nikolakis had no time to puzzle out such subtleties. He had another errand to do that morning. He changed his collar and combed his hair, and then set out for Panayia.

The Phillipides' were glad to see him, for the night before they had heard disquieting news. But this visit was hardly any consolation. He burst into their courtyard, delivered them the very same oration on the subject of his duty he had just delivered to the Yeroyioryis', and then, a moment later, departed as suddenly as he came.

"What did he say?" said brother Petros.

"He said, for the time being, he cannot marry Fifika after all," said Captain Markos.

"Cannot marry her?"

"He said he cannot marry her until his sister finds a husband."

"Until his sister finds a husband? But why didn't he think of that before? You don't think the Yeroyioryis' have a hand in this? You don't believe what they were saying in the town last night, that the doctor's *proxenia* was announced in Ayia Marina yesterday, to Marika Yeroyioryis?"

"How could that be," said Captain Markos, "when it was concluded to my own Fifika? You were right here when I concluded it."

"I thought so too."

"He sat right there on that stool and told us only a madman would decline to have Fifika."

"So let us hope he is not a madman."

"Of course he's not," said Captain Markos. "He sat right there and told us that no man in his senses would decline to make his life among us with fair Fifika for his wife."

"So let's hope he's in his senses," said brother Petros. "But unfortunately that was not the impression I had of him this morning."

"Of course, he's in his senses! He meant to say that he will marry my Fifika. There's no mistake about that."

"Maybe he meant to say it," Petros said, "but all the same, I would feel more comfortable if he *had* said it."

"Nonsense, to show such brotherly concern for an unmarried sister is evident of a faithful nature. And a faithful nature is a virtue, in case you haven't realized it, even in a husband."

"I have nothing against virtue in a husband," said Petros, "as long as he's a husband. Let Dr. Nikolakis marry our Fifika first, then he can be as faithful as he wants."

But all the Phillipides' could do, in their courtyard in Panayia, was to wait and see, which was precisely all the Yeroyioryis' could do in their courtyard in Ayia Marina. Even Dr. Nikolakis had done all he could, and for the time being, he went home for a night of badly needed rest.

That evening there was no moon. Two black-cowled old ladies, Sofitsa and Kalitsa, were sitting on a threshold in Ayia Marina, when three apparitions passed by their gate, a lantern flickering before them.

"*Proxenia!*" said Sofitsa.

"I wonder who," said Kalitsa.

On silent slippers, Sofitsa and Kalitsa went out into the street,

and there they saw the three figures were Captain Manoli
Yeroyioryis and his two brothers, who stopped at the house
of another old seafarer of Ayia Marina, Captain Kakoyanis,
whose first son Andoni was still a bachelor.

"They've given up the doctor," Sofitsa whispered. "You don't
need theology to know that. Now, to save face, they are hurry-
ing to conclude their daughter's *proxenia* with Andoni Kakoyanis."

But Sofitsa was wrong, and not even theology would have
helped her know the answer. The Yeroyioryis had not given up
the doctor, not at all. It was true their moonless mission was a
proxenia, but not on behalf of their daughter Marika. They
had come to ask about Andoni Kakoyanis' hand in marriage,
not for their own Marika, but for a young Kasiot girl who was
in no way their relation, not yet, in any case. They were performing this *proxenia* on the authority of the doctor's mother,
and the girl whose hand they offered to Andoni Kakoyanis was
the doctor's sister, Eloula.

Though Eloula had been too young for marriage in the
morning, by sunset her time had come. Dr. Nikolakis, sleeping
peacefully for the first time in two days, awoke the next morning to hear musicians announcing his sister's *proxenia*.

The next Sunday was the first of three Carnivals. On the last
three Sundays before the beginning of Lent, people went
around the streets in masks and antic costumes, eating and
drinking far into the night. But this Sunday, people in Ayia
Marina celebrated a double feast, for besides the usual festivi-
ties of the day, they celebrated the *emvasmata* of Andoni and
Eloula.

First, the combined families gathered at the Kakoyanis'
house for the signing of the *prikosimfonon*. After Andoni's had
been signed, Dr. Nikolakis rose to recite his sister's. (What
could he do? He had appealed to custom, and now he must
follow wherever it should lead him.)

"In the name of the Father and of the Son and of the Holy Ghost," he began, in the traditional form of the Kasiot *prikosimfonon,* "in this fair and benevolent hour which has come upon us, I, Dimitri Nikolakis hereby establish familial relations between myself and Captain Yani Kakoyanis of Ayia Marina and accept his first son Andoni as a bridegroom for my pure and virgin sister Eloula. First I give her my blessing, and the blessing of our mother and of all our family, and then I give her all the following: the house she lives in and all its contents, including 6 blankets, 12 bed sheets, 4 pillows and 8 pillowcases . . ."

It was a laborious recitation. No one was interested in pillows and bedsheets. What everyone was waiting to hear was the sum of hard cash that would accompany Eloula's hand.

But Dr. Nikolakis was saying nothing about cash.

"A vineyard near the cemetery," he said, "a grazing plot below Arvanitohori and a field of barley near the western bank on the rain-torrent. In addition, on behalf of my mother who ardently desires to be with her loving daughter both in her dotage and beyond the grave, I designate one vineyard near the Chapel of St. George of the Spring to be withheld as a *yerontomoiri.*"

Now, at last, undoing a wine red handkerchief, Dr. Nikolakis let its contents fall on the table before the notary.

"In addition," he said, "I give her fifty golden sovereigns."

It was a modest sum, and it produced a modest murmur. But it was almost the total cash resources of the Nikolakis family. Dr. Nikolakis surrendered it freely, since in a very short time, if he married either Fifika Phillipides or Marika Yeroyioryis, he would receive many times that total in return.

"Fifty golden sovereigns," said the notary, after counting out the coins. "Is it agreed?"

"Agreed!" said Andoni Kakoyanis.

"Agreed!" said Andoni's mother and father.

"Agreed!" said all the *demogeronts* of the island and other influential elders.

Now the *prikosimfonon* was signed and ready to be put away in the island's archives. From the rear of the *salla* came the sound of violin, *laout* and lyre, the musicians striking up a rhythm to lead the assembly out into the narrow streets of Ayia Marina to wind their way to the Nikolakis' house where Eloula would be waiting for her bridegroom-to-be.

Three Kasiot ladies led the march, holding candles before them. Immediately behind them came the musicians, with violin, *laout* and lyre. Behind them, arm in arm, marched the two male principals in that pageant, the bridegroom Andoni and his best man, Dr. Nikolakis. Finally, winding in and out of the tortuous village streets slowly as a *sousta*, came the long line of all the relatives of the bride and groom, the *demogeronts* of the island and other influential elders.

There were maskers in the streets, out for the first Sunday of the Carnival. White gypsum masks peered out of open doorways. Other inhuman apparitions peered around the corners of dry-stone walls, human bodies with heads of pigs and donkeys. Barefoot children beat stones against tin cans. Other villagers set off fireworks and fired pistols at the sky. And everyone in the procession joined in a call as universal as "Christ Has Risen."

"*Gambros!*" they cried, with one voice, as on the Resurrection. "*Gambros!* The bridegroom! *Gambros!*"

It was a call as joyful as that announcement on Easter Eve, for *gambros* in Greek means bridegroom, and by that call the people were announcing yet another bridegroom, the incarnation of another Unknown God, the coming of yet another messenger of light, whose arrival was a kind of Resurrection, bearing the promise of procreation and rebirth.

When they reached the Nikolakis' house, the candlebearers took their places on one side of the gate, the musicians on the other. Behind them, the entire procession parted, lining either side of the narrow lane. Inside the gate, Eloula stood with downcast eyes, radiant in the white dress she would wear at her wedding. Beside her stood her matron-of-honor, Yani's wife, holding the silken quilt she would throw down beneath the feet of the bridegroom as he stepped across the threshold. Now, approaching his moment, Andoni marched arm in arm with his best man, Dr. Nikolakis. There was no music now, no pistol shots or fireworks, no shouts of bridegroom. Dr. Nikolakis let go Andoni's arm, for a best man could lead the bridegroom only to the threshold of his *emvasmata*: the step across it the bridegroom must take alone. Now all Kasos was quiet in anticipation. On the whole island, there was only a gentle sound of rain as maidens sprinkled rosewater on the bridegroom's head. Calliope unfurled the silken blanket beneath the bridegroom's feet, and then, jumping over it and across the threshold, Andoni Kakoyanis landed in the courtyard of his intended bride.

By now, there was a bitter rivalry between the Phillipides' and Yeroyioryis'. They were both so exasperated by the doctor, they wished they had never made a proposal to him in the first place. But now, neither family could give him up without admitting defeat. For each family it was Dr. Nikolakis at any cost, if not to win their daughter's happiness, at least to save face before the island.

In the meantime, Eloula's wedding day was drawing closer. The next day, musicians mounted on donkeys led some of Eloula's cousins to every house in the five villages, inviting every family.

Before each door from Ayia Marina to Poli, the donkeys halted and the young men and women called out into windows shuttered above the road: "You are invited."

And from every window, through shutters opened in response, the reply came down: "And to your weddings too, in time, those of you unmarried."

"And to your children's weddings too, in time," the young men and women replied in turn. "And to your grandchildren's after them."

In the meantime, the pace of preparations quickened for the coming feast. Every night that week, women kept a late vigil at the Nikolakis' household, folding thousands of *dolmades,*° the staple of any Kasiot celebration. The day before the wedding, three oxen were brought up from Phry, decorated with tassels and ribbons like Resurrection lambs. And that night, few people slept. The early spring moon rose over Ayia Marina, almost full. The sky was so clear the stars seemed to be standing still. Lanterns flickered late in the surrounding houses, and through the shuttered windows came murmurs of anticipation: an occasional laugh, a muffled female voice. Keeping late vigils on the thresholds, black-cowled philosophers mused over weddings of the past and weddings yet to come.

The next day, everyone in Kasos was inside the Nikolakis' gates. The courtyard was full of bobbing bow ties and colored kerchieves. Before the marriage table, laid with golden cloth and candlesticks from Constantinople, stood Father Minas, the priest of Ayia Marina. Before him stood Eloula in her laces and veils and Andoni in his frock coat, and behind them stood the best man, Dr. Nikolakis, and the matron-of-honor, Calliope.

Quietly, Father Minas intoned the silent prayers, abridging them a little as all priests do those prayers intended only for the ear of God. Then, he raised the crowns of lemon above the two submissive heads.

"The servant of God Andoni is crowned for the handmaiden of God Eloula," he sang. "The handmaiden of God Eloula is crowned for the servant of God Andoni. In the name of the Father and the Son and the Holy Ghost. Amen."

Behind the couple, Dr. Nikolakis moved the crowns back and forth above their heads. In the Orthodox wedding, the best

° Vine leaves stuffed with meat and rice.

man must switch the crowns three times, so that at the end of the ceremony, the groom's crown will be on the bride's head and her crown will be on his.

The priest murmured the final prayers, and the couple drank from the common cup, leaving the best man to drink the rest.

Then, suddenly, the priest cried out: "Rejoice, O Isaiah, the Virgin hath conceived and brought forth a son! Holy martyrs, you who have fought bravely and been crowned . . ."

The priest took Eloula's hand, and she took her husband's hand, and her husband took the matron-of-honor's hand, and she took Dr. Nikolakis' hand. One after another they danced around the wedding table. There was laughter in the courtyard now. The congregation rained rice and cottonseed on the couple, and slapped Dr. Nikolakis hard on the back. Faster and faster the priest pulled Eloula, and Eloula pulled Andoni, and Andoni pulled Calliope, and Calliope pulled Dr. Nikolakis. Faster and faster they danced Isaiah's Dance. And Dr. Nikolakis was pulled along after them, three times around his sister's wedding table.

The oxen roasting on the spit were cut down and carved and served with steaming rice and Kasiot dolmades. And throughout the feast, the musicians sustained the wedding rhythms, to the insistent whining of violin, *laout*, and lyre.

The feast lasted late into the night. By the time the guests had gone, bidding the couple their last good wishes, the spring moon, full as a wineskin, had sunk below the mountains. Now the last custom of the evening was performed. Captain Kakoyanis and Dr. Nikolakis led the wedding couple to their new house and locked the door behind them.

The next day, on thresholds throughout the island, black-cowled prophets mused on the events to come.

"Whatever happens," Sofitsa said, "one of the girls will marry the doctor before this week is out."

"How do you know?" said Kalitsa.

"Simple," said Sofitsa. "Next Sunday is the third Carnival, and the day after that is Pure Monday, the first day of Lent. And after Pure Monday, no marriage is permitted until the end of Lent, after Christ has risen. But the Phillipides' and the Yeroyioryis' cannot possibly wait that long. Even now, they can hardly meet in the street without drawing guns, so if they had to wait for forty days, they would surely kill each other. They will do anything to settle this affair before the beginning of Lent, and since, according to our religion, the doctor can marry only one of them, then *one of them will marry him before this week is out.*"

"I see," said Kalitsa, scratching her head.

But Sofitsa had reasoned soundly, as far as she could. This Pure Monday, the whole island would be watching these two maidens' doors, to see which one would have a padlock fastened there. And each family would do anything, even violence, to avoid that shame.

On Tuesday morning, the Phillipides' arrived to pay a call on Dr. Nikolakis. When they arrived, he was still asleep. Outside his shuttered windows, Mother Nikolakis received them curtly, without the customary offering of candied fruit. She told them the doctor was not there.

"Not here?" said Captain Markos. "Where is he, then?"

"Some place else, apparently," said Mother Nikolakis. "He didn't give me a report. He's old enough to come and go without telling his mother where he's going."

So the Phillipides' departed to search for the doctor in one of the other villages. A little later, the Yeroyioryis' came, and they too found the doctor still asleep.

"He's not awake yet, but it's time he was," said Mother Nikolakis. "I'll send for him immediately."

And so she called Eloula to wake her brother and tell him that the Yeroyioryis had come to see him. Eloula, lately become the mistress of a separate house across the courtyard, ran this errand for her mother as dutifully as ever. A moment later, she returned.

"He's not here," she said.

"Not here?" said Mother Nikolakis. "Where is he then?"

"Some place else, apparently," Eloula said. "He didn't give me a report."

"Squashes and cucumbers for your report!" said Mother Nikolakis. "Go and find him and ask him what he means by going off without telling his mother where he's going."

So the Yeroyioryis', too, departed to search for the doctor in one of the other villages. But the strange fact which they discovered, as the Phillipides' discovered it ahead of them, was that the doctor was not in any of the other villages. Though they searched for him in every corner of habitable Kasos, Dr. Nikolakis was nowhere to be found.

What had happened was as follows. The day before, the Monday morning after Eloula's wedding, musicians had gone around the island announcing the doctor's *proxenia* to Marika Yeroyioryis. Then, having made one round, they went round again, announcing his *proxenia* also to Fifika Phillipides. In this way, the only double *proxenia* in history sounded over Kasos in a jangled discord.

The first *proxenia* was no news to Mother Nikolakis, but the second caused her much outrage and dismay. As soon as she heard it, she descended on her son.

"What about this Fifika?" she said. "What about Fifika Phillipides?"

"What about her?"

"Why are the musicians announcing that your *proxenia* to her is concluded?"

"Because it is."

"But I already told you, it is concluded to Marika Yeroyioryis."

"I know. And it is also concluded to Fifika Phillipides. It is concluded to both of them."

"To both of them?"

"Yes."

"But how was it concluded to Fifika Phillipides? Who concluded it?"

"I did."

"You did? But how could you do that?"

Dr. Nikolakis explained the impossible: the same afternoon when his mother accepted the proposal of the Yeroyioryis', he himself had accepted the proposal of the Phillipides'. But still his mother did not understand.

"But why should you conclude your *proxenia* to Fifika Phillipides?" she said.

"Why? Because I wanted to marry her."

"You wanted to marry her? You wanted to marry Fifika Phillipides?"

Dr. Nikolakis nodded.

"You wanted to marry Fifika Phillipides on your own accord?"

Dr. Nikolakis nodded again.

"And you thought that was all there was to it? You thought you could just go off and conclude your *proxenia* to someone just because you wanted to marry her, without telling me a word about it until afterward when it was already too late?"

"Too late?" said Dr. Nikolakis. "Too late for what?"

"Too late to stop it, of course. You didn't think I would possibly agree to such a thing? You didn't think I would simply accept the fact that you went off and decided to get married?"

To this question, Dr. Nikolakis had no answer. In a dark way, he had been troubled by it himself, though he did not know why he should be.

"So this is my reward after all I've done for you," his mother was saying. "To see you ask a girl to marry you on your own accord. Fifika Phillipides indeed! Why her father and her uncles must have fallen off their stools, delighted to get that hussy off their hands."

"She's not a hussy," said Dr. Nikolakis. "She's a respectful and obedient girl. She is the first daughter of a first daughter, descended in direct lineage from a noble Kasiot family."

"Squashes and cucumbers for her lineage," said Mother Nikolakis. "She's a hussy. She must be, to make you agree to marry her against your will!"

"I did not agree against my will. I agreed on my own accord."

"So much the worse. She must be a witch, to make a man agree to marry her on his own accord."

"Anyway," said Dr. Nikolakis, "you're the one who's trying to make me marry against my will. You are forcing me to marry Marika Yeroyioryis."

"That's different," said his mother. "Marika Yeroyioryis is not a hussy. She's an obedient and respectful girl, the first daughter of a first daughter, descended from a noble Kasiot family. And what's more, it wasn't her idea to marry you, it was *my* idea. If it hadn't been for me, she never would have thought of marrying you, even in her wildest dreams, and you would never have thought of marrying her. But let me tell you something. You will marry her all the same, even if I have to stand behind you with a gun. You will marry her and live with her in that house of hers which you can see from here, right next door where I can keep an eye on you. And that's all I have to say on the subject of your marriage."

And that was all Dr. Nikolakis had to hear, for he had just become a revolutionary. Could a man be forced to marry against his will? Was it marriage, to kneel before a tyrant, to wed himself to a puppet bride? Could marriage be forced at gun-point, the crown lowered on his head by the hand of tyranny itself?

Now that Dr. Nikolakis had pronounced his dogma, he knew his course. Of the two daughters, he would marry the one he wanted. Fifika Phillipides was the girl for him, as she had always been. He would marry her as he agreed in the first place. That was his way to marry, on his own accord, and if it wasn't in keeping with the Kasiot custom, then squashes and cucumbers for the Kasiot custom.

That Monday night, one week before the fatal Pure Monday, Dr. Nikolakis waited for the time until the lights were blown out in all the houses of the island and the only sounds were stray dogs howling on the mountains and the unending sea washing the iron shore. Then, after midnight, he made his way through the darkened streets of Ayia Marina, downhill past the cemetery, through the back streets of Phry, until the road emerged again and rose uphill to Panayia on the other side.

There, at Captain Petros' house, Dr. Nikolakis knocked on his brother Yani's door. He asked Yani to lead him to the sheepfold in the hills, and with a smile, Yani agreed. He led him past the chapel of St. Elias, opposite the town of Arvanitohori across a huge canyon opening like a lesion in the rock. And there, in a sheepfold sheltered from the wind, Dr. Nikolakis found his hiding place. The next morning, when first the Phillipides and then the Yeroyioryis' arrived at his house, Dr. Nikolakis, the child of custom and tradition, had vanished forever from the island, and a new Dr. Nikolakis, partisan of revolution, was hiding in his place.

After swearing his brother to secrecy, he entrusted him with a message for the Phillipides': he had been called away to cure an epidemic in Karpathos but would marry Fifika as soon as he returned. In the meantime, he planned to stay hidden in the sheepfold until Pure Monday. He was well aware of what the families had been saying, that they would have the doctor's hand or have his head. And he knew if he tried to marry Fifika Phillipides before Pure Monday, he would risk being shot by the Yeroyioryis'. Dr. Nikolakis saw no need for that. Even in the cause of freedom, he saw no reason to risk his life. After Lent was over, the Yeroyioryis' would be calmer, and he could marry as he pleased. He would marry Fifika without delay, as soon as forty days were over.

But the Phillipides' did not understand. Fatally, they could not tolerate this last excuse. By that time they were frantic. They knew, just as the Yeroyioryis' knew, that the doctor could not have gone to Karpathos, for the island steamer had not put into Kasos since before Eloula's wedding, and in the meantime, not one caique had left the island, even for a day. So the doctor must be on the island after all.

In the final hours of the third Carnival Sunday, a terror reigned on the island. Two families roamed the villages, and as peace-loving Kasiots trembled before their guns, they upset furniture in *sallas*, turned over pots and cauldrons in cook-houses, ripped out bedding in *moussandras*, all in search of their chimerical Dr. Nikolakis.

And now, at the story's end, Yani played a final role. From Thermopylae to the sack of Kasos, every Greek story must have a traitor. There is always an embittered soul who knows the cleft between the mountains and leads the enemy to treachery, whether they are Medes or Turks or Phillipides'.

Yani was embittered because he found that marriage was not what he expected. Far from being beautiful after all, he found his wife Calliope really was too short. And far from being cheerful and good-natured, she was as feeble-minded as every-one had said. Yani found, as husbands often find to their dis-may, that though the role of bridegroom is the most heroic in the world, the role of husband is a tragic-comic one at best, a mere supporting role. And at that point, after this discovery, Yani wanted to make sure his brother shared his fate.

When Yani arrived at the sheepfold in the hills, the sun was already down on the third Sunday of the Carnivals. There were maskers abroad again: nymphs and centaurs, satyrs and nereids, and urchins carrying padlocks to leave on unmarried maidens' doors. But of all the maskers abroad that night, none wore a more impenetrable disguise than Yani Nikolakis.

The doctor suspected nothing. What should he suspect since in those waning hours before Pure Monday, there could be no more *emvasmata,* no nuptial table set, now that the time of marriage was sealed away.

"He's sick," said Yani, "old Petros Phillipides. He's trembling so much, I think his soul must be between his lips."

Swiftly, foolishly, Dr. Nikolakis came. Taking his bag of medicines, he mounted the mule behind his brother. Down from the hills near Arvanitohori they rode, both of them on one saddle. Down they rode to that deserted plain, sharply rutted with volcanic rock. On they rode, Yani shouting to the mule and striking its haunches with his whip. And now Dr. Nikolakis was beyond recall by any mortal on the island.

Outside the Phillipides' house, they dismounted and went the rest of the way on foot. They marched down the path toward the courtyard gate, arm in arm. There, as Dr. Nikolakis reached the Phillipides' threshold, Yani let go his arm, leaving him to take the final steps alone. The next moment, crossing the threshold as blithely as a bridegroom, Dr. Nikolakis stepped into the range of a dozen Phillipides' guns.

"What's this?" said Dr. Nikolakis.

"Your wedding," said Captain Markos.

"My wedding? At gun point?"

But Dr. Nikolakis received no answer except Captain Markos' handkerchief stuffed into his mouth. Surrounding him were all the Phillipides': brothers, uncles, cousins. In the center of the courtyard was a wedding table. Behind it, more Phillipides' pistols at his back, stood Father Minas. In front, supported by a cousin on either side, was a fainting girl: Fifika in her wedding gown.

Her wedding portrait was hardly flattering. Her body was limp, her head fallen forward, the coins of her dowry threaded on her breast like chains. They pushed Dr. Nikolakis beside her, his hands bound behind his back. From that moment, the handkerchief still in his mouth, Dr. Nikolakis embraced his fate in silence.

It took just a few minutes.

Father Minas abridged this service more skillfully than any in his career. "The servant of God Dimitri is crowned for the handmaiden of God Fifika . . ." he sang. "The handmaiden of God Fifika is crowned for the servant of God Dimitri."

Brother Stavros, the best man, switched the crowns over the couple's head, his pistol gleaming in the moonlight. Dr. Nikolakis was crowned for Fifika and she was crowned for him, and the next moment, a Phillipides pistol thrust suddenly into the small of his back, Father Minas cried out: "*Rejoice,* O Isaiah, the Virgin hath conceived . . ."

It was time for Isaiah's Dance around the table. The priest was prodded forward, and so was Dr. Nikolakis behind him. But in her fainting condition, Fifika had to be carried. By either arm, her cousins lifted her off the ground and moved her around the table, like a puppet. It took a long time for the cumbersome party to complete three circles, and afterward there were no gifts pinned to Fifika's gown, no *mandinadhas* sung in honor of bride and groom. Solemnly, pistols raised and gleaming in the moonlight, all the Phillipides' kissed the wedding crowns.

Then, it was time for the final custom. They carried Fifika to her new house and pushed Dr. Nikolakis after her. They laid her on the gold-embroidered sheets, lifeless as a corpse. Then, loosening Dr. Nikolakis, they locked the door behind them. Finally, in a most uncustomary procedure, they gathered around the house to peep in between the shutters.

Inside, Dr. Nikolakis looked at Fifika. A few hours earlier, he had been hiding in the hills, plotting how to marry her without being shot by the Yeroyioryis'. And now, unexpectedly, he had succeeded. With the fulfillment of his wishes within his reach, Dr. Nikolakis sat on the sofa opposite her bed, saying to himself: *Can a man be forced to marry against his will? Could a marriage be forced at gun point, the crown lowered on his head by the hand of tyranny itself?*

And that was how Dr. Nikolakis worked his woe, insisting on a principle poignantly inappropriate. That was how the roads to wedlock parted before him once again, and how he finally chose revolution at exactly the wrong time. Though he had been married at gun point, it was not to Marika Yeroyioryis but Fifika Phillipides. Though the hand of tyranny indeed had held the crowns, it had crowned him in wedlock—of all people—to the girl he wanted. At that point, the judicious course, even for a revolutionary, would have been to throw down his flag at the maiden's feet and proceed according to the custom.

But Dr. Nikolakis did not. Throughout history, there have been two kinds of revolutionaries: those who change their principles according to the circumstances and are revisionists, and those who cling to principle and are dogmatists. Dr. Nikolakis was a dogmatist, and like any dogmatist, he could embrace the cause but not the maiden. Like any new recruit in freedom's struggle, Dr. Nikolakis found it easier to raise his flag.

He rested on his dogma and declared: "Before this tyrant, I will not kneel."

Meanwhile, the Phillipides' were whispering at the shutters. "What's he doing?"

"Sitting on the sofa," said Captain Markos. "His arms are folded. He will not approach."

"Will not approach?" cried the others. "But that's outrageous! We'll not allow it."

"Very well then," said Captain Markos. "But what can we do?"

In the meantime, in the bower, something very surprising was happening to Dr. Nikolakis. Suddenly, without any warning, Fifika woke up. She sat up straight in her bed, and opened her eyes to discover the doctor sitting at her feet. Suddenly, in that one moment, all Dr. Nikolakis' doctrine was undone. To his amazement, Fifika was not a puppet after all! She was a living girl, the one he had chosen as his bride! And how beautiful she was! Why had he not discovered that before? Her face was white as milk, her black hair falling down around it in perfect ringlets. And those eyes! They rested on him so directly, so personally and intimately. They looked so bewildered, so humble, so noble in their unwillingness to reproach him.

"What have you done?" they seemed to ask him, gently, unchidingly. "Why do you let them do this to me?" And in that one instant, a flood of feeling rose in Dr. Nikolakis' heart. Only a madman would decline to have this girl! No man in his senses would refuse this maiden for his wife! He wanted to run to her, to embrace her, to beg forgiveness. More than anything in the world he wanted her. Finally, Dr. Nikolakis knew, as he had never known before, that Fifika Phillipides was the girl he wanted for his wife.

But at that moment, at the window, other dogmatists were clamoring in outrage, raising a banner of their own in the face of changing facts.

To an enraptured man in loving contemplation of his bride, they shouted through the shutters: "We will not stand for that!"

To a bridegroom paralyzed with wonder, gazing on the girl he loved, they shouted: "We'll not permit such outrage!"

The next instant, the Phillipides' burst through the windows, firing pistols.

"Out of here," they shouted. "We'll have a husband for our daughter, not a faggot!"

Dr. Nikolakis jumped through the window and landed in the courtyard below. Fifika, conscious for long enough to see her family come in firing pistols, and her lately married husband depart a moment later through the same window, sank into oblivion again.

Around her, the Phillipides' danced like demons.

"Gone," said a Phillipides brother at the window, watching Dr. Nikolakis sprint through the gate and out into the streets of Panayia.

"Let him run to hell," shouted another Phillipides. "We'll find another bridegroom for our daughter, and he'll marry her this very night."

He meant, of course, that without consummation, the ceremony was an empty ritual, the crown a hollow crown. They would find another bridegroom to take the doctor's place, and they would find him before the night was done. Once again they gathered Fifika in their loving arms and lifted her from her wedding bed. Mounting mules, they carried Fifika on their shoulders like a corpse in bridal clothes. Holding a lantern to light their way, they set off on the road to Phry, shouting: "A bridegroom for our daughter! *Gambros* for our Fifika! *Gambros! Gambros! Gambros!*"

Meanwhile, Dr. Nikolakis was covering ground toward Ayia Marina. He didn't know why he was running, but he was running just the same. He passed maskers on the way, out for the final revel. They stood aside for him—Turkish pashas, Jews in pillowed pantaloons, satyrs, nymphs and centaurs— all made way for the strangest creature abroad that night, a bridegroom running from his wedding bed.

Uphill the doctor held his pace, up the road beyond the Bucca, past carob and olive branches gleaming in the moonlight chimerically as ghosts. Then Dr. Nikolakis came upon a band of maskers who would not make way. He didn't see them until he had run straight into their midst, then he saw them all at once, the way one sees an image in a dream: one incomprehensible vision made up of unrelated parts. There were a dozen bandits, shouting and waving pistols. In the midst of them was a priest, and beside him, seated on a mule, a young woman in bridal clothes: Marika Yeroyioryis.

"Well, Dr. Nikolakis," said Captain Manoli Yeroyioryis.

"We've been expecting you. We wonder, what custom you can conjure now to prevent your marrying our daughter."

"A simple one," said Dr. Nikolakis. "I'm married."

"Married?" said Captain Manoli.

"Married," said Dr. Nikolakis. "To Fifika Phillipides. My regrets, gentlemen. A previous engagement you understand."

"On the contrary," said Captain Manoli, thinking quickly, speaking now not only to Dr. Nikolakis, but to the grandstand of the island and all posterity. "We must offer our regrets to *you*. We are embarrassed to meet you here, since technically your *proxenia* was still concluded to our daughter. But I must tell you frankly, when you stopped us now, we were on our way to our daughter's wedding. She will be married this very night to another."

"Then long life to her," said Dr. Nikolakis.

"And long life to you," said Captain Manoli Yeroyioryis.

And so, the Yeroyioryis' took their leave of Dr. Nikolakis for the last time. Dragging their helpless daughter after them, and Papa Minas to his second wedding of the evening, they also descended to the town of Phry.

They were the first to reach the café above the Bucca. (The Phillipides' had spent time searching for Papa Minas.) There, above that placid bowl, a rowdy symposium had lasted late into the night. Two roistering philosophers, Pavlos the tailor and Kosta the cobbler—both of them late into their forties and still unmarried—were discussing the subject of the day.

"I'd rather never marry," Pavlos said, "than sell my heart for a house and dowry. Pavlos the tailor will wait for love."

"And what will you do with it?" said Kosta the cobbler. "Can you eat it? Will you wear it? No, one girl is as good as another and even the gorgon has her charms. But the reason I have never married and probably I never shall, is that I've never heard of a dowry large enough to tempt me."

"And how much would be required?" said a voice at the head

of a large party riding mules right up to the café. "How much would be required to tempt you with the hand of Marika Yeroyioryis?"

"Marika Yeroyioryis?" laughed the cobbler. "The one who is engaged to Dr. Nikolakis? And who is offering her crown to me?"

"Her *father*," said the newcomer, pointing his pistol at the cobbler. "And as for your Dr. Nikolakis, such a girl as my Marika is beyond his wildest dreams."

"*Your* Marika?" said the cobbler. "Well, then, I must beg your pardon. But if she is beyond a doctor's dreams, she must be beyond my dreams as well, for I am but a poor cobbler, and at this moment, a drunken one."

"A cobbler is an honest trade," said Captain Manoli, "and as for being drunk, that is not a disadvantage. Any man must be a little drunk to marry, and once you are a husband, you won't take long to sober up."

The cobbler scratched his head and understood that it was not simply his imagination, that it was really Marika Yeroyioryis bound to the mule beside her father, and that her father was actually offering him her hand. "In that case," he said, "how much is offered?"

"A hundred sovereigns," said the captain, "and all her mills and fields."

"Only a hundred?" said the cobbler. "They say the doctor was offered five hundred and he refused."

"From the Phillipides'!" roared the captain. "With such a prospect as their daughter, they had to borrow money to get her off their hands. From the Yeroyioryis', the doctor was offered nothing, and so had nothing to refuse."

"In that case," said the cobbler, smirking, "I must consider. For a hundred sovereigns, I need time to think."

"In that case," replied the captain, pointing the pistol at the cobbler's head, "you have twenty seconds."

"Twenty seconds? And after that, what then?"

"And then you will be shot."

"Shot?"

"Through the head."

"Through the head? Well, in that case, I need no more time to think. For a hundred sovereigns, I agree."

"Agreed!" shouted Captain Manoli.

"Agreed!" shouted all the Yeroyioryis' and the drunken elders of the Bucca.

As Papa Minas performed the service, Marika Yeroyioryis was crowned for Kosta the cobbler, and he was crowned for her. The crowns were handed around the party for every drunken mouth to kiss, and as the revellers wished long life to them, the new couple were locked up in a back room of the café.

"Shameful!" said Pavlos, on his dogma. "Pavlos the tailor will wait for love."

"Then wait no longer," said another newcomer, leading another mounted party to the café. "Love is here."

This time, the priest thought he had gone mad. He thought he was seeing double. He thought he had fallen under a curse always to be haunted by these fanatical families. First he must marry off Fifika, then marry off Marika; then, after he married off Marika, here was Fifika once again.

"Here she is," the Phillipides' shouted, handing down their daughter. "Here is the girl you have waited for all your life. You are the bridegroom for our Fifika. You are her *gambros*."

"*Gambros!*" said the Yeroyioryis', and they too believed they were seeing ghosts. "Your daughter has no *gambros?*"

"Not now, but she is soon to have him," said Captain Markos. "She is about to marry Pavlos the tailor."

"But what about Dr. Nikolakis?" said Captain Manoli. "He was married to your daughter tonight."

"In his dreams perhaps," said Captain Markos, "though not even there, for such a girl as my Fifika is beyond the doctor's dreams. Pavlos the tailor, do you agree to marry this girl, with a hundred sovereigns to accompany her?"

While Pavlos the tailor deliberated, Captain Markos leveled a pistol at his head.

"I agree," said Pavlos.

And that is how two noble Kasiot daughters, two princesses of the island, were given away, one to a cobbler, the other to a tailor. And that is how two Kasiot sophists, less subtle than Dr. Nikolakis, won the prizes he had lost, realizing what he had not: that freedom has nothing to do with marriage in any case, and if a man is out to consummate a wedding, the flag of freedom must eventually come down, and some kneeling before the tyrant must be done.

And so, Dr. Nikolakis married neither daughter, neither Fifika nor Marika. After the final bride departed, he sat down, exhausted, by the dry-stone wall. The next morning he would return to Ayia Marina, to live with his mother until she died, fulfilling the prophecy recited in golden tones that there was no girl on Kasos worthy to become his bride. But that night, he slept beside the dry-stone wall, beside a prickly-pear as contorted as a bridegroom's road to marriage, beneath a hump-backed olive gossiping in the wind. And the next morning, when Pure Monday had dawned and urchins smirked to see the mischief of the night before, Dr. Nikolakis awoke beside the dry-stone wall, his arms folded on his breast, and a padlock fastened around his neck.

Greek Flag
Over Kasos

*T*he journey is almost over and Kasos has a hundred and eighteen years to go before it will become Greek. In 1830, in London, Kasos was excluded from the new Greek nation. In 1832, it was returned to Turkey. And now, through the nineteenth century, its *xenitia* was more bitter than ever. Now there was a Greece beginning at the Gulf of Arta and extending southeast across the Cyclades. But farther south and farther east, beyond the enchanted boundary, lay Kasos and the rest of the Dodecanese. As a reborn Greece began its new life, Kasos began another chapter in its everlasting exile.

In the decade following the Revolution the town of Phry was built along the shore. But it took more than a decade for the population to reach what it had been when the island was sacked by the Egyptians, and about the same time for a Kasiot merchant fleet to replace the one towed away by Ismael. By that time, Kasos was never again to aspire to the future as it had in 1821. One hundred miles south of the Greek border, Kasos was a remote province of the Ottoman Empire, a mercantile and cultural backwater. Her children began to abandon her, sailing off into *xenitia*.

The first of them sailed north to Syros, which had become the metropolis of the Archipelago. At the end of the eighteenth century, Syros had hardly a thousand people, most of them Uniates or Eastern Rite Roman Catholics, leftover from the days when the island was Venetian, known as Syra. In 1821, Greek Catholics saw no reason to fight a revolution so that an Orthodox ruler could replace the Moslem. Like other Catholic islands, Syros remained neutral, paying taxes both to the revolutionaries and the Turks; and from this neutrality, it was to reap great advantage. Syros became the refuge for many Greeks from other islands, and by the end of the Revolution, its population had grown to forty thousand. Not only was Syros included in the new Greek nation, it had become a provincial capital. It had Greek schools and government offices; and since it was located where many Mediterranean sea lanes intersected, it became a merchant center: until this century, the largest port in Greece.

Like Elias of the Fez, Kasiots sailed to Syros to register their ships with the Greek authorities and gain the right to fly the Greek flag. Many of them stayed on, to educate their children in Greek schools, or simply for the privilege of living in Greece. At the same time, Kasiots began to emigrate southward. Eight years after de Lesseps founded the Suez Canal Company, there were six thousand Kasiots living near the isthmus. Throughout the nineteenth century, the emigrations continued, to Africa and Australia, to Canada and the United States. Though there are 1,650 Kasiots on Kasos today, there are over ten thousand living in *xenitia*.

On the native island, life continued much as it had in the preceding centuries. Forgiving his prodigal subjects, the Sultan reaffirmed the ancient privileges. The *Demogerontia* ruled

Kasos as it had before, paying a yearly tax to the Pasha of Rhodes. In 1867, there was a revolution in Crete and the incorrigible Kasiots sent arms to support it. As a result, the Sultan decided that Kasos and the rest of the Dodecanese must each have a Turkish *Kaimakami* or governor to keep a watch on the islanders' activities. Nevertheless, this *Kaimakami* could not interfere with the work of the *Demogerontia,* and he obtruded so little into the life of the island, that as Aphrodite remembers, he said good morning to the islanders in Greek.

In 1908, the Young Turks overthrew the Sultan. Eventually they tried to rescind the privileges of the Dodecanese. They devised an administration for the islands, proposed to levy increased taxes, and for the first time in history, held the islanders liable for service in the Turkish Army. But the Young Turks had no time to put these intentions into practice. The Dodecanese was about to be taken from them, and the final, darkest chapter of Kasos' exile was about to begin.

In 1912, the Balkan Wars broke out, and by 1913, when the last peace was signed, Greece had achieved the greatest territorial expansion in her history. On the mainland, the Greek armies had won parts of Macedonia and Epirus. To the south, Greece gained the island of Crete, autonomous since its final revolution of 1898. Once again, as in the early years of the Revolution, the Greek fleet sailed supreme in the Aegean, liberating islands one by one. In a single year, Chios, Samos, Lesbos, Lemnos, Samothrace, and Thasos all became Greek. If the Greek fleet had been able to sail into the Dodecanese, it too could have been liberated and the dark night of Kasos would have ended.

But that night was not to end, not in 1913. The Greek fleet did not sail into the Dodecanese because the Italian fleet had already occupied it. In 1911, Italy had gone to war with Turkey over Cyrenaica and Tripolitania on the North African coast, and as a strategic maneuver she sent her fleet to occupy the

Dodecanese. On their arrival, the Italians gave out two stories. They told the Turks they would keep the islands only as long as the Turks threatened their North African possessions. On the other hand, to the Greek islanders they posed as liberators. General Ameglio, the Italian commander, declared on arrival: "The Turkish supremacy has ended on Rhodes and on the other islands, and the future of the islands cannot be other than their autonomy. . . . After the termination of the Italo-Turkish War, these islands temporarily occupied by Italy will receive an autonomous system of government . . . and the Turk will return no more. This I say as a general and as a Christian, and you should believe my words as words of the gospel."

The islanders believed him. Ingenuously, they called a congress of delegates on the island of Patmos to draft a resolution and laws for the self-government of the Dodocanese. After hearing a Liturgy in the Cave of St. John the Evangelist, the delegates issued a proclamation of autonomy, naming the new island nation The Aegean State, establishing the laws of Greece and customs of each local community as the law of the land, and declaring their wish for *Enosis*. Poignantly enough, they even devised a provisional flag to fly over the islands until the Greek flag could be raised: a blue field with a white cross and the portrait of Apollo.

But the Dodecanesians were soon to realize that like the gospel, General Ameglio's words were open to different interpretations. What followed for them was a tortuous road through the subtleties of Italian diplomacy, and they were to emerge not in the autonomous state promised by Ameglio but under the fascist government of Mussolini.

By the Treaty of Lausanne of 1912, the Turks were to evacuate Tripolitania and the Italians were to evacuate the Dodecanese. But in fact, neither party observed the treaty. While matters stood in this uncertain state, World War I broke out, and after remaining neutral at the beginning, Italy declared war on the

Central Powers in 1915. The secret price for this allegiance, agreed upon in London, was to be the Dodecanese.

So the Italians were staying in the Dodecanese after all. They told the Turks that the World War voided the Treaty of Lausanne of 1912. To the Greek islanders, on the subject of Ameglio's promises, they said nothing. Actually, that made the Dodecanese technically Turkish, since the Italo-Turkish War of 1911 had not been formally concluded. Finally, in 1923, Italy signed a new treaty with Turkey, another Treaty of Lausanne, by which—to the amazement of the Dodecanesians—Turkey formally ceded the Dodecanese to Italy.

The blue field with the white cross and the portrait of Apollo never flew over the Dodecanese. The Patmos Proclamation turned out to be as empty an essay in self-government as a straw vote among children. And in 1924, after living out of a suitcase for thirteen years (out of an attaché case), the Italians were unpacking for good.

By that time, Mussolini had come to power in Rome, and a fascist government was set up for the Dodecanese which did not feel bound to honor the ancient privileges granted by the Turks. By decree in 1924, the Italian Governor-General of the Dodecanese kept all powers exercised by him until then, that is, the powers of a commander in a military occupation. Sub-governors were appointed to rule groups of islands under him, and a marshal and a detachment of *carabinieri* were posted on each individual island. In all respects, the autonomy of the islanders was a dead letter. The *Demogerontia* still collected taxes, but now there was no limit as there had been under the Turks. The islanders could still elect their *demogeronts*, but they did so from an approved slate of candidates; and at any time, the Italian authorities could dissolve the *Demogerontia* and call for new elections. Legally, the islanders were considered Italian *subjects* and not Italian *citizens*, a distinction which provided the rationale for most of the violations of their civil rights. The road to power and privilege was open to them only if they became Italian citizens, and to do so, they must join the Fascist Party. Few islanders exercised this privilege, and those who did were despised and ostracized by their fellow Greeks.

Otherwise, the islanders had no civil rights. They could be sent into exile by decree, or moved about from one island to another. They could not travel abroad without permission, and this permission would not usually be granted them. Their property could be confiscated to be used in the construction of military bases and tourist hotels or simply awarded to settlers arrived from Italy. Their businesses were eventually curtailed, including the sponge-fishing industry which had thrived on Symi and Kalimnos. (During that period, Symiots and Kalimniots founded the large sponge-fishing community which exists today in Tarpon Springs, Florida.) Eventually, Dodecanesians were even required to serve in the Italian Army, against the Loyalists in Spain, with the Italians in Ethiopia, and finally against the Allies in the Second World War. In this service, it must be said, their record was not distinguished.

But in ruling the Dodecanese, the Italians were to make two errors which the Turks had scrupulously avoided. They attacked Greek culture and the Orthodox religion. National demonstrations were forbidden. Greek holidays must pass unobserved. No Greek flag was to be flown anywhere in the Dodecanese, and no houses or churches could be painted blue and white. (By some oversight, the house with the blue shutters miraculously survived on Kasos.)

First, the authorities made the study of Italian compulsory in the island schools. Then, they required all instruction to be in Italian while Greek was studied only as a foreign language. Against this invasion of their culture, the islanders had a simple defense: they kept their children out of school, a form of patriotism island children willingly embraced. In the first year of the new policy, school enrollment dropped sharply, and before long, most of the Dodecanesian schools were closed. Some students received instruction secretly from tutors, but most of them simply remained uneducated, a loss which they had to repair as best they could, after the end of Italian rule.

The attack on the Orthodox religion was more devious, requiring the tacit allegiance of the Church of Rome. In 1919, there was an Easter rising in Rhodes. A village priest emerged from church holding in one hand a Bible, and in the other, a resolution of *Enosis* for the Dodecanese. Around him the villagers shouted not "Christ is Risen!" but *"Enosis!"* The ancient identification of Greek nationality with the Orthodox religion, sealed in the Greek mind by centuries of Moslem and Roman Catholic rule, was being stated once again. The Italians responded by bayoneting the priest in his robes and killing a woman and a boy in a demonstration elsewhere on the island. That day, the Italians realized, if they had not known it before, that if their rule in the Dodecanese was to be secure, the resistance of the Orthodox Church must somehow be broken.

Accordingly, they devised a plan to bring the church under their control. First, they would detach the Dodecanesian Church from the Ecumenical Patriarchate at Istanbul by making it *autocephalous* or independent. In that way, the Metropolitan of Rhodes would be the ruler of the church, independent of the patriarch at Istanbul, and he would therefore be able to appoint priests and bishops at his discretion. Since he was resident in Rhodes, he would be subject to coercion by the Italian government; and in this way, he could be forced to appoint Uniate priests and bishops to take the place of the Orthodox, thus delivering the Dodecanesian church into the Roman Catholic hierarchy.

Apostolos, the Metropolitan of Rhodes, was the key figure in the plan, and in 1921, the Italian government banished him to Patmos and kept him imprisoned there for three years. During that time, with Italian encouragement, he came to appreciate the eventual advantages of collaboration: not only his freedom from persecution, but the fact that if the Dodecanesian church were to be *autocephalous,* as its head he would have to be promoted from Metropolitan to Archbishop. In 1924 Apostolos was released from Patmos, a would-be archbishop and a collaborator with the regime. He applied to the Patriarch for *autocephalous* status for his church, entering into a complicity which made him anathema to his spiritual children. The Patriarch replied that he would grant the request only if a plebiscite were held in the Dodecanese to determine the will of the people. The plebiscite was never held.

Failing in these negotiations, the Italian government attempted to achieve its ends *de facto.* Orthodox priests and bishops were forced to resign, and Uniates were appointed in their places. Those Orthodox who objected were imprisoned, and soon the island jails were full of beards and robes.

But the Italians did not achieve their purpose that way either. Out of the many centuries of foreign rule, all that bound the Dodecanese with Greece was language and religion. After so many centuries of tenacity, it was unlikely that Dodecanesians would let go now. The islanders responded to any innovation in their religion by rioting. When a Catholic wafer was substituted for the wine of the Orthodox communion, the result was bloodshed at the altar. Ultimately, the islanders preserved their freedom of religion the same way as their language. If they could not go to church to hear an Orthodox liturgy, they would not go to church. In a short time, most of the island churches were closed, and those churches where Uniates presided were empty.

Like the subjects of the Ottoman Empire who pretended to have apostasized to Islam, the islanders preserved their faith in secret. Until the Italians had departed from the islands, the Dodecanesians held their marriages, christened their children, and buried their dead, with secret rites.

But this is not a story of oppression, but of exile, of the

xenitia of an island and a people. There is one point about Italian rule of the Dodecanese which is relevant here. In 1912, when the Italians arrived, the population of the Dodecanese was 143,000. In 1944, when they left, it was 100,000. On those islands more prone to emigration by a tradition of seafaring, the discrepancy was more dramatic. In 1912, the population of Symi was 23,000; in 1944, it was 2,000. In 1912, the population of Kasos was 7,000; in 1944, it was 900.

In the thirty-one years from Ameglio's arrival to the Italians surrender in World War II, a third of the population of the Dodecanese had vanished into *xenitia*. They rowed off in open boats, among the Italian coast guards, into the blackness of the night. After reaching the coasts of Asia Minor, they made their way to Smyrna, where they took a steamer to a Greek island and finally arrived in mainland Greece. Afterward, in their everlasting diaspora, they spread to all the corners of the world.

Now, in this final chapter of the island's exile, the expatriated islanders had their chance to play a role. The battle for the Dodecanese was ultimately fought out, not only by Greek and British commandos entering the islands in the waning days of the war, but by Dodecanesian-Americans—shopkeepers, tradesmen, and professionals—in New York City. For the last chapter in the story, we return to the scene of the beginning, to those groups of expatriated islanders, banded together in an adopted land.

In 1934, when an earthquake in the Dodecanese made many people homeless, Dodecanesian residents of New York met with the Orthodox Archbishop at his office in Astoria to make plans to send assistance. It was the first time they had met each other. Until then, they had been isolated in their *xenitia*, in the sea of immigration of New York. But that snowy night, as they came out of a Queens subway station, they formed a group which was eventually to agitate for the *Enosis* of the Dodecanese.

Symbolically, their first meeting was held under the aegis of the church, just as in the years before 1821, the Revolution was plotted by priests in their churches. Later, the headquarters was moved to a barbershop on Eighth Avenue owned by a Dodecanesian, where thirteen islanders founded the Dodecanesian League which put out *The Dodecanesian,* a monthly newspaper in Greek and English, agitating for *Enosis.*

In 1939, the Dodecanesian League was transformed into the Dodecanesian National Council. Assisted by donations, mostly from Kasiot shipowners recently arrived in New York, it moved to an office in Rockefeller Center, hired secretaries and clipping services, and went on with its work of propaganda, putting out *The Dodecanesian* and writing letters to the press and members of the American government.

The leaders of the movement were all expatriate Dodecanesians, and some of them had even been born in *xenitia.* The first president of the league, James Polychronis, was born in Istanbul of parents expatriated in turn from the island of Nisyros. Nicholas Mavris, another leader, (editor of the Archive of Kasos) was born in Zaghazig in Egypt.

The Dodecanesian National Council was the only organization anywhere agitating for *Enosis.* Dodecanesians remaining on the island naturally could not speak for themselves, and up to 1941, even the Greek government would not speak for them, hoping to the very last to remain on friendly terms with Italy.

At one point, an official of the United States Justice Department informed Dr. Mavris that he and the council would have to register as agents of a foreign power.

"I agree," replied the doctor, "but *what* foreign power? The Greek government will have nothing to do with us. There is no Dodecanesian government. Surely you don't believe we are acting on behalf of the Italian Government. I think you'll just have to say that we are crazy, and we're shouting because we're crazy."

The rest of the story is the story of the Second World War. By

1936 there were thirty-five Italian warships and two hundred Italian planes harbored in the Dodecanese. In addition to garrisons and airfields, the Italians had built submarine stations and an airbase on Leros under hundreds of feet of rock where planes could take off and be in the air before they emerged from shelter. The islands were continually under martial law; Italian troops passed through them every week on their way to Ethiopia, then arrived a short time later, on the way back, to rid themselves of malaria before being transported back to Italy.

In October 1940, in the wake of Hitler's successive victories, Mussolini delivered an ultimatum to Greece to submit within three hours. The answer was the famous "No!," heralding an astounding upset in which the Greek army with British support not only expelled the Italian invasion but advanced into Albania where the Italians had been entrenched. Meanwhile, in the Aegean, after being routed by the British fleet off Cape Mattapan, the Italian fleet withdrew harmlessly into its Dodecanesian harbors, leaving the British to cruise the Archipelago at will.

Then Hitler came to Mussolini's aid. In April 1941, the German Army crossed the Greek border, proceeded down the Vardar River and broke the line of Greek resistance. The Greek army capitulated; the Greek Government took refuge first in Crete and finally in Egypt; and the British Expeditionary Force withdrew. Greece was under military occupation.

For the next two years, the two Axis Powers divided control of the nation between them, the Germans ruling Crete and most of the mainland, the Italians adding most of the islands of the Archipelago to their command at Rhodes. Then, in 1943, Italy surrendered to the allies. At the time, there were 18,000 Italian troops in the Dodecanese and 8,000 Germans. But incredibly enough, it was the Germans who disarmed the Italians. Though the Italian rule in the Dodecanese had come to an end, the Germans were able to hold out.

After the Italian surrender in 1943, the Dodecanesian National Council sponsored a gala dinner to proclaim the *Enosis* of the Dodecanese. Italian rule in the islands was at an end. But in the meantime, there were still some anxious moments. There was a danger, which no Dodecanesian dared express, that the proclamation of this dinner in 1943, like the Patmos Congress of 1912, and the treaty of 1829, would be rescinded by events to come.

Here, of course, is where the work of the council proved most crucial. What happened in the conference rooms of western Europe was as beyond the islanders' control as what happened in 1830. But by the council's work, public opinion had been educated. This time, the result of the conferences left nothing to be desired. By the Treaty of Paris of 1946, the Dodecanese was ceded by Italy to Greece. The next year, Greece was empowered to appoint a military commander. And after one year of military administration, on March 7, 1948, at a ceremony in Rhodes, King Paul of Greece proclaimed *Enosis*.

So in 1948 the long night was at an end, the long exile came to its conclusion. After being in foreign hands since the beginning of the fourteenth century, Kasos and the Dodecanese were finally redeemed. For the first time in history, the Greek flag— a white cross on a field of blue, against a background of blue and white stripes—was flying over Kasos.

There is always a little sadness mixed with joy in the fulfillment of any dream. Now Kasos had become a Greek island, living in the present instead of in the future, a remote outpost of the Archipelago, thirty miles in area, with a population of 900 which grew eventually to 1,650. After 1948, it was part of the administrative unit of the Dodecanese which sends five deputies to the Greek Parliament. From that time on, its aspirations were not historical but actual. It aspired to build an ample harbor so that the steamer could come alongside a jetty instead of discharging its passengers into open boats. Now that the harbor has been built, Kasos aspires to get the steamer to come to the island more than once a week, so that islanders afflicted with a sudden illness can be transported swiftly to the hospital at Rhodes. It aspires to get some of the expatriated Kasiots in the world at large to return and rebuild their houses. It aspires, ultimately, to build a road connecting one end of the island with the other.

In America, the Dodecanesian National Council was disbanded. Most of the original leaders had died, many of them before they saw the result of their efforts. As I sat with Dr. Mavris in his study in Athens, and with Mr. Polychronis in his office at the corner of Central Park, I became aware of what they had relinquished with the fulfillment of their dream. Outside the doctor's study, workmen were tearing up the Athens Street. Outside Mr. Polychronis' office, traffic rounded Columbus Circle. The world was carrying on its work, and whatever these two men had done—especially because their efforts had been successful—was laid securely in the past.

Mr. Polychronis showed me a photograph from his files. It was of the dinner held by the council in 1943 to celebrate the Italian surrender and to proclaim—prematurely but inevitably—the *Enosis*. The photograph was taken in a banquet room of the Hotel St. Moritz, which because of its Greek management had become a meeting place of the Greek expatriate community. It showed several hundred Dodecanesians, assembled at tables according to the island of their origin. At the head table I recognized the Archbishop, Dr. Mavris, and other directors of the council. And at a table among other Kasiots, looking not much older than I am today, I saw my mother and father.

That night when my parents drove into New York City to this banquet of their ancestral island, I was at home by the golf course in Rye. As my parents departed into that world unknown to me, I was left at home, in an enduring *xenitia*.

It took twenty more years for me to see the Greek flag over Kasos. There is some sadness in that discovery as well. Once again Kasos has become just another island. Kasos is an island where the vengeance of a virago was like any other vengeance, where a man might plan to marry but finally did not. Kasos ultimately is an island, where the price of eggplants was higher than on Rhodes.

Departure

*W*e were to leave Kasos on the ship for Rhodes. It was supposed to arrive at six in the morning, but a storm came up the day before, and if the wind persisted, the boat would simply omit Kasos from its weekly run and go on to Rhodes without us. One way or another, we wouldn't know until morning, when the ship was scheduled to appear.

Our last night in Kasos was an anxious one. With our bags all packed—the plastic bags and shirt cardboards and rubber-bands stuffed back into Uncle George's suitcase—we sat on the veranda and watched the sea. Across from us, the peaks of Karpathos were fading in the distance. Below us, darkness crept over the courtyard where my namesake had been married to Eleni Mavroleon, where a midwife had held up their first son George, and where, to celebrate his christening, mezitia had been flung against the sky. For the rest of the evening, villagers came to say farewell. One old lady, who had a daughter living in America, came accompanied by a young man from the café, who carried a crate of *koulouria**° for her. She accepted a candied fruit and a glass of water from Aphrodite. Then, after wishing us a good voyage, she told us she had a favor to ask.

"Will you take these *koulouria*," she said, "to my daughter in Jackson Heights?"

My uncle looked puzzled.

"Will you take these *koulouria* to my daughter in Jackson Heights?"

"But I am not going to Jackson Heights," said Uncle George. "I don't live in America anymore."

"But your nephew does."

"Ah, yes, of course, my nephew does," said Uncle George, in dead earnest. "He can take them on his way home."

I looked at Uncle George in amazement. Of course, I could take them: in the hand I reserve for carrying bananas. I came with bananas, I could return with *koulouria*. As a fertility symbol, I had become hermaphroditic, eastward male, westward female.

I told the old lady I would take the *koulouria* to her daughter, and she blessed me and bade us farewell.

After she had gone, I didn't even have time to say anything to my uncle, when an old gentleman appeared, carrying a large metal container. He too accepted candied fruit and wished us a good voyage, and he too had a favor to ask.

"Will you take these honey-frittles to my cousin in New Jersey?" he said.

"Of course," said Uncle George. "My nephew will take them on his way home."

"Of course," I said.

The old man blessed me and bid us farewell, and as he went away I thought: *fear the Kasiots bearing gifts.*

No more villagers came to pay us their respects, and for the rest of the evening we had to contend only with Aphrodite. She was hovering around us, on imaginary errands.

° Dry Kasiot doughnuts, made of barley-flour.

"If you take that ship tomorrow, you'll drown for sure," she said. "And I won't weep for you, believe me. It'll serve you right anyway, for bringing me back to this ruined island. In Alexandria, I had a house of my own and Arab servants to call me 'Kyra Aphrodite.' And you brought me back and shut me up alone, in this house, so I could end my days waiting for the roof to fall in upon my head. So you came back to Kasos, came back to my Eleni's house? And just as I said, you're ready to sail away again on the next ship. What do you want with Kasos, you and your nephews. Tomorrow you'll sail away, and I'll never see you again. After you go, I'll be left alone."

"We'll be back," said Uncle George. "We'll come back to see you."

"Come back to see me? When? In another fifty years? I won't be here then, and neither will the island. In fifty years, this island will be at the bottom of the sea, where it belongs. When you sail by in the ship to Rhodes, you'll see nothing but blue water. Anyway, I don't want you to come back. I was glad to see you, but I'm an old woman and I can't weep the way I used to. I don't want you to come here ever again, because I don't want to weep for you when you go."

With that, she went into the other house, to hide her tears.

Uncle George and my cousin and I sat in silence. The peaks of Karpathos had vanished. Across the courtyard, in the farthest corner, we could see a lantern Aphrodite placed there every night, to help nocturnal vagrants find their way, burning like a votive light to Vasilios' lost archives. The town was quiet. As we settled back to our gloomy contemplations, Uncle George did not help dispel our mood. With such forebodings of catastrophe in the air—of death by drowning and islands descending beneath the sea—he remembered his last voyage as captain of his father's ship, when he was shipwrecked.

"What happened on that voyage, Uncle George?" I said, providing my usual cue.

"What happened on that voyage? I'll tell you what happened. We were shipwrecked."

"Shipwrecked? And what do you remember about it?"

"What do I remember? I remember *dolmades.*"

"*Dolmades?*"

"Yes, wonderful *dolmades,* the sweetest I have ever eaten. They were made from vine-leaves grown near fresh water, by a spring near Port Said, and the fresh water made them exceptionally sweet."

"How did you happen to have these *dolmades?*" I said, "on that voyage when you were shipwrecked?"

"Not *dolmades,*" he said. "One *dolma.* I had only one of them, and then the ship's whistle sounded and we all made for the lifeboats, and I nearly went on the long journey with the taste of that wonderful *dolma* in my mouth, and all the others lost forever."

So Uncle George told the story of his shipwreck in 1916, returning to Greece from India, the story of his final voyage as captain of his father's steamship, before he retired from the sea to spend the rest of his life in shipping offices, first in London, then New York, and most recently Piraeus.

His ship was named the *Lily,* a three-island steamship, so called because of its three islands: fo'c'sle, bridge, and poop. He sailed her up the Red Sea, through the canal. Then, in Port Said, he stopped to join a convoy. In those days, in 1916, the Mediterranean was infested with submarines, and one of them in particular, *Port Said Jack* had become the terror of the waters between Egypt and the Greek islands. For every convoy that departed from Port Said, one ship was sure to be sunk. *Port Said Jack* struck only once, then vanished as suddenly as he appeared, to elude any depth-charges. And so, that December of 1916, each captain wondered if his ship had been chosen by the fates. The crews were all advised to keep their belongings packed and be ready to abandon ship. And the British trawler, accompanying the convoy, made ready to pick up survivors.

"In Port Said, a relative gave me the *dolmades*," said Uncle George. "Beautiful sweet *dolmades*, all warm and steamy in a jar. I tasted one of them. Delicious! And then my Uncle John, my father's brother, who was sailing with me, took the jar and put it where I couldn't find it. All day, I looked for it. And that night, *Port Said Jack* struck us, and our ship went down and the *dolmades* with it."

"Was anybody lost?"

"No, only the *dolmades*. The trawler picked up all hands. As soon as we were safe I asked Uncle John what he had done with the *dolmades*. 'Why did you hide them?' I said. 'So that you could have them for later,' he said. *Have them for later?* Well, he saw what happened. There wasn't any *later*. I nearly went on the long journey with the taste of that wonderful *dolma* in my mouth and the thought of all the others to torment me for all eternity. Uncle John was so parsimonious. He was an incorrigible saver."

"There is saving and saving," I said, looking at the tin of honey-frittles and the crateful of *koulouria* I had so suddenly acquired.

By now, I had decided I must make a deal with Uncle George. This curse had become too dreadful. I am so fastidious with hand-luggage, I must have been singled out for special torment: first bananas, now honey-frittles and a crateful of *koulouria*.

"Make up your mind," I said to him. "It's either the *koulouria* or the honey-frittles. One of them must stay."

And so we made a compromise, an accommodation between the two instincts descended in my family, from Vasilios the saver and Old Yia-Yia the disposer. We decided to take the honey-frittles which were easier to carry, and left the *koulouria* where they belonged, in the alcove off the living room, with their counterparts the bananas. And therein, in that fateful choice, lay the source of my own catastrophe at sea.

In the morning, the sea was calmer, though not calm enough. The summer wind in the Aegean always dies at night, but if there is any wind in the early morning, as the day wears on there is sure to be a storm. At five o'clock the ship was sighted, turning stubbornly in the uneasy sea. The peaks of Karpathos were just showing through the morning mist. Above the highest of them hung a puff of white cloud: an ominous portent.

"In two hours, you'll be drowned," said Aphrodite, risen in her spotted bathrobe, the white kerchief around her head. "Tonight we'll be singing dirges for you."

The car arrived, at the end of the row of dilapidated balconies. After loading the car, we turned back to say good-bye to Aphrodite. She was standing at the gate. Before her, the three of us stood sheepishly, like children.

"Go," she said. "Go quickly."

We said good-bye.

"Yes, yes, good-bye, good-bye," she said. "Good-bye to George. Good-bye to the two Eliases. Good-bye to Aphrodite."

And so we went. We left her where we found her, by a blue door in a wall of white, standing watch over an empty house.

At that moment, the ship's whistle sounded, and our departure was imminent. Out of a light on the sea, the ship had emerged full-blown, advancing steadily toward the harbor. Though we knew we had plenty of time, we were apprehensive, so unfaithful to our ancestral island, we were afraid to be abandoned on it. The car rattled through the empty streets, past the placid pool of the Bucca, past the belltower with the clock. The town was asleep, colorless in that hour before the sunrise, its windows shuttered except for the vacant ones, watching our departure in perfect equanimity. We boarded the ship without ceremony, and as the ship slipped out of that unattended harbor, at six o'clock, exactly on schedule, Kasos was behind us.

A few minutes later, as soon as we were clear of the island, we met catastrophe. The wind came up, and the ship began to roll.

In the open water toward Karpathos, the sea became a field of demons. The ship plunged one way and then another. Very soon, sitting staunchly on the bridge, I felt as sick as any rabbi.

"A storm after all," I said to Uncle George.

"A good one," he said.

I sat against the railing, my face buried in my sleeve. Meanwhile, Uncle George narrated to the wind.

"Later, Uncle George," I said. "Later please."

I thought we would never make it to Karpathos. There were moments I wanted to jump overboard, to put an end to my misery. I had to keep perfectly still, eyes closed and face covered, to avoid the slightest physical effort, even to listen to Uncle George or to look at anything around me.

In the meantime, Uncle George was chattering.

"*Koulouria* are very good for that," he said.

"For what?"

"For what you are feeling now . . . for sea-sickness."

And then I remembered. Once on an earlier summer, I was in a storm off Syros, and when I thought I was going to be sick, someone gave me a *koulouri* to chew on and I felt marvelously better. The dough of the *koulouri* is so dry and hard, it absorbs all the rancors of the stomach, and Greek sailors use it instead of dramamine.

And then I understood my fatal error. I had taken the honey-frittles instead of the *koulouria*. I had left all those marvelous *koulouria* behind which would have worked my cure, and in their place I had taken honey-frittles, sticky and sweet and sickly. And so, like Uncle George, I was tormented with imaginings: a gross of Kasiot *koulouria*, rare therapeutic delicacies, abandoned forever on the island.

That way, I was unaware of the moment when Kasos disappeared. Though I had been imagining that departure for many years, when I came to make it, I wasn't even looking back. Two hours later, when the ship sailed into the lee of Karpathos and the wind subsided, when I looked around at last, Kasos was gone. I never saw it vanish, just as I never saw it appear ahead. On arrival, Kasos was born unperceived out of the mists on the horizon, and on departure, it slipped unnoticed into them again.

Two weeks later I was in New York. Uncle George had returned to his office in Piraeus for another winter, and in the following year, we continued our conversations by long distance. I had left him the tape-recorder, Aphrodite's genie. On my side of the Atlantic, I got another one. And now, instead of filling long pages with his tiny hand, Uncle George had only to summon the genie, turn him on, and speak.

By that time, I had begun this book, and as the earlier chapters were completed, I sent them to Uncle George and asked for his comments. It took him a long time to reply. There was something wrong with the genie, and he'd sent him to be repaired. Finally, weeks later, a tape arrived.

At first, I wondered how he would take to our new medium. I wondered if he could be comfortable before a microphone, speaking into a genie's indifferent ear. But when the first tape arrived, I did not wonder anymore. Ever since dictaphones have been in use in business world, Uncle George has used them passionately. When he was working in New York, I used to see him in his office, sitting among several conversations going on around him, mumbling endless monologues into a metal ear. Now he spoke to me across the ocean exactly as though dictating a business letter.

"My dear Elias," he said, "*comma*. I received your letter today asking for my thoughts on the chapters which you sent me *period*. I hope you will agree that it would not be proper for me personally to dare to make corrections, but reading your book, I see that certain facts have been completely changed, for example in the chapter which you entitle 'The Way to Phry.'"

As he became involved in what he was saying, he forgot to

specify the punctuation, except occasionally. After a while, out of a tape-recorder whose silent rotations made circular reflections on my ceiling, Uncle George simply talked to me from his office in Piraeus. Every so often, behind his desk, I could hear the shutter rattling in the harbor wind.

"Perhaps it was my fault in not having described everything carefully," he said. "For this purpose, I will repeat the story of our return from Syros and my parents' departure for Egypt, exactly as I remember it."

Another Way to Phry, I thought. I had put on the tape at about midnight; at two o'clock, Uncle George was still talking.

"The *Anastasia*, you remember, was in Syros with a cargo of roof-tiles, chartered at five francs a ton. 'What do you expect to do with five francs a ton?' my father's brother asked him. As you have stated in the book, we used to tease Mavrandonis, floating his hat in the soapy water. And mind you, he was the terror of the sailors. They were very good sailors, and often they finished their work very quickly, and he had nothing more to give them. In those days, we kept a hog on board. Whenever the sailors finished their work ahead of time, Mavrandonis would tell them, 'Go and bring the hog on deck. Poor creature, he needs some air.' Then, the next day, if they finished their work again, he would say, 'Take the hog below. Poor creature, it will die of cold.' The sailors grumbled, 'Up with the hog, down with the hog.' And that became a proverb among us, for any sort of futile labor. Even now, I often tell my wife, when she constantly rearranges the furniture in our living room, 'Up with the hog, down with the hog.'

"When peace was declared, my father prepared to deliver the roof-tiles to Russia, and then go on to Alexandria with my mother taking baby Nicholas and Maria with them. Basil and I were sent home to Kasos in a caique, not in the *Anastasia*. So you see, what you have written is wrong that the *Anastasia* anchored in the lee of Makra Island long enough for us two boys to be sent ashore. The *Anastasia* did not return to Kasos. On our way back in the caique, I remember stopping at the island of Astakia which belongs to Kasos: a small rocky island. We went there to look for water, and we found a pool of rainwater and filled one or two casks to enable us to continue on to Kasos. Two of the crew brought out fishing lines, because in the crystal clear water, we could see some pretty large fish playing at the bottom.

"Now another thing. That day when the *hapari* of Aunt Virginia arrived from Alexandria, Old Yia-Yia was not in Kasos. She also had gone to Alexandria because of Uncle-Doctor's engagement, and she was there when Aunt Virginia died. One of our neighbors was in charge of us. She had the keys to our house, used to come and see us every day, and sent a man to the market to buy food for us. She was the mistress of the house when the *hapari* came, and she—not my grandmother—must have been sitting at the center of the circle on the terrace. What Aphrodite says is nonsense: that my grandmother took Basil and me to throw us down the well. She could not have done it because she wasn't there. Aphrodite was talking through her hat, probably thinking of Medea sacrificing her sons for vengeance."

So what I have written is wrong. The *Anastasia* did not anchor in the lee of Makra Island, and the caique did not go out to meet her. Eleni and her two boys did not ply that windy passage, and the boys did not hold the gunwales like brave cavaliers, riding the white horses home to Phry. Some weeks later, when the *Dhekeli* returned from Alexandria and the two boys picked their way home to their unshuttered house to learn of the *hapari*, it was not Old Yia-Yia in the center of the circle on the terrace. It was not Old Yia-Yia with her cowl thrown back and her hair hanging down in tormented strands. It was not Old Yia-Yia, but the woman who lived next door.

As the truth is revealed, it reveals the mischief of the mind. The first mistake occurred between Uncle George and me. I never asked how he returned to Kasos, only assumed it was on the *Anastasia*. The second mistake was more complex. Uncle George heard Aphrodite's story of Old Yia-Yia and the well, and at first, he did not know enough to question it. Then, in the second telling, his memory emerged. Old Yia-Yia was not in Kasos but in Alexandria; otherwise, the neighbor woman would not have held the keys. This time, the mistake was Aphrodite's. Remembering the story after sixty years, she insisted on what did *not* happen as firmly as though she could see it in her mind's eye. She had simply confused the story with a myth. She had heard of Medea in her childhood, and drawing that story from a past more ancient, she imposed it on the more recent one. Maddened by the news of her daughter's death, says Aphrodite, maker of a modern myth, Old Yia-Yia, the merciless Medea, tried to drown her grandsons.

As the truth is finally uncovered, the layers above it are revealed, layers accreted in the decades following the events. Though we know all the stories in their entirety, we do not know how they may have changed. I could make a careful inspection of my notes to determine what Uncle George actually told me and what I made up out of my own assumptions. And before that, Uncle George could rack his memory to determine what Old Yia-Yia or Aphrodite or Mavrandonis actually told him. But before that, further inquiry would be impossible. Prior to Uncle George's memory, no verification can be made. We cannot resurrect Old Yia-Yia or Mavrandonis to ask them what they remember, and Aphrodite—the only other surviving narrator—is so perfected in mythopoeia, she can no longer distinguish fact from myth. The facts themselves lie beyond memory. Somewhere beneath this growth of decades, like the original seeds from which plants have grown to renew themselves each year, the facts are lost in the rocky bed of Kasos, irrevelant to the stories that have grown from them.

So after circling the island, we could go around it once again.

As the plastic spool dispenses Uncle George's voice, it spins another Kasos. On this second turning, the light hits Kasos from a different angle, and we see aspects of the island we missed before. This time we see the island of Astakia, north of Kasos and west of Karpathos, where Kasiot shepherds used to take their flocks to graze. We see Mavrandonis' hog, the bane of the *Anastasia's* crew, preserved in proverb long after his demise so that he roots on, incongruously, in Uncle George's living room. We see a spring, with crystal clear water, and fish chasing each other around the bottom.

This way, the journey never will be over. Aphrodite's gloomy augury may come true—that with the passage of time, Kasos will slip back into the sea—but that would make no difference. Kasos does not lie between Crete and Karpathos, except in reality. The gloomy prophetess may be right—there may be only blue water there some day—but in that Aegean of the future, we shall still be sailing round.

Since there is no arrival or departure for us, no beginning and no journey's end, since we are doomed to sail the sea interminably between the past and future, I can leave the journey only in a way-station.

From Rhodes, Uncle George and I returned to Athens. Some days later we went to spend the afternoon with an old Kasiot woman who lived an hour outside of town. She was over ninety, but in good health and in perfect possession of her memory. Like my old aunts in Syros, she had come from Kasos sixty years before and was living out her *xenitia* in an Athenian suburb. Her son is a shipowner who lives in London, but she preferred the hills of Attica, where she lived with a daughter to take care of her. She had not seen my uncle in many years, but she greeted him as though he had been to visit the week before. He introduced me in the usual Kasiot mode, as Elias of Michael. But either this statement of my lineage did not mean much to her, or she felt my age disqualified me from any communication with her. For either reason, she acknowledged my presence only with a nod, and for the rest of the afternoon, she did not say a word to me or even look in my direction.

We were shown into the dining room. The old woman sat in the corner in her black dress and cowl, and Uncle George sat beside her. I sat some distance away, across a table. On the wall above the woman's head, I saw a tinted photo of her son, in a business suit and an austere pose appropriate to the city of London. Outside, sprinklers cooled the lawn in a burning August afternoon. The shutters were all closed against the heat, and inside, with its stone floor and wooden furniture without upholstery, the room was cool and dark as a tomb.

The old woman and Uncle George began to talk. They did not seem aware of me. And very soon, I spread my arms on the table, rested my chin on my hands, and watched them.

I remember no matter how old Uncle George and Aphrodite had become, they still had the same relationship. In the same way, I realized that whenever one comes on certain scenes of childhood, one feels exactly the way he did as a child. Now, listening to Uncle George and the old Kasiot woman, I felt as I had in childhood, overhearing one of those ancient, unintelligible conversations of my house in Rye. For a moment, I felt as I had before, perhaps accompanying my father on some unfathomable errand, waiting to get on to some business I could understand. As I listened now, for a moment I heard the liquid polysyllables which had once been so bewildering, Romaic echoes of the past.

But now I could understand. The syllables composed a language.

Still they did not observe me. Still they ignored me perfectly. As I sat in the accustomed attitude of childhood, chin on my hands, I felt as I had before, too young to know what they were talking about, too ignorant even to ask a question. I didn't make a sound, only turned my uncomprehending face toward them, my own understanding hidden behind it as completely as the tape-recorder—Aphrodite's genie—had been hidden beneath the table.

The old woman was telling about the customs of the island, about the custom of *proxenia* and *emvasmata*, of naming children, of wailing dirges for the dead. She told about a feast known as *Kleithona*, about a certain doctor who couldn't decide which of two girls to marry, and about a vengeance.

That was the final surprise. I knew it all. I knew the stories they were telling, and the customs. I had heard it all before. As I watched them, my chin cradled in my open palms, I knew at last—if I could have had any doubt of it—that childhood was over. There were no more unknown stories for me, no more mysterious words.

But unaware of this, not seeing the silent watching face across the table, the old woman turned to Uncle George.

"By the way, George," she said, "that reminds me. My grandson told me a very disturbing thing. He said you told him the story of your great-grandmother, Hazimanolis' widow, and he said you told him the widow wanted Basil Kikos dead because she'd slept with him, once when Hazimanolis was away at sea, and now she took this opportunity to have him killed and bury her shame."

Uncle George was astounded. Even I, across the table, blinked. Just as I predicted, one of the cats was back already: a monstrous, deformed copy of the original. But, ironically, it was one my uncle had not engendered.

"Impossible," said Uncle George. "I could not have said that because it is not true."

"Are you sure?"

"Of course, I'm sure. How could I have said it? I heard the story from many different people and I never heard that from anyone. The widow wanted Basil Kikos dead, because according to the vengeance, his death must pay for her husband's death. An eye for an eye, a life for a life."

"All right, George," the old woman said, "I believe you. My grandson must have gotten it wrong somehow. Or else, he just made it up to tease me."

The old woman paused a moment, peering to the limits of her shuttered world. Then, still seeing only George, still not perceiving the stranger from another world, his own demon making silent circles in his head, she told my uncle:

"But it makes me think George, maybe from now on we'd better keep these stories to ourselves. Maybe we'd better not talk about the past so much, at least when the young people are around."